PEARS

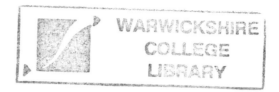
PEARS

by Jim Arbury
Illustrations by Sally Pinhey

Wells & Winter
Mereworth
Maidstone ME18 5NB
1997

ISBN 0-9532136-0-9

Printed in Great Britain by
Butler and Tanner Ltd.
Frome and London

FOREWORD

Jim Arbury has filled a long outstanding need concerning the cultivation of pears with this book on the identification of the fruit. Each cultivar in this work is comprehensively described and beautifully illustrated with water colour paintings by Sally Pinhey. He has detailed over fifty cultivars. There are others, but he has selected those that the gardener or commercial grower in this day and age is most likely to come across in the gardens and orchards of Great Britain. An additional virtue is that he himself has handled each and every one of them as they are all grown in the pear collection at the Royal Horticultural Society's Garden, Wisley, Surrey, which is under his care.

Mr Arbury has also included characteristics not usually employed in identification such as the weight of the fruit and the length of the leaf petiole. The principal purpose of the book is, of course, fruit identification. Nevertheless, Mr Arbury has also given some useful information on pear culture, for example pollination and rootstocks, and he has made mention of Asiatic and perry pears.

I commend this book to the interested gardener who wants to know the name and learn the origin and history of the pear grown in his or her garden, and to all those, for whatever reason, who need to identify pears grown in the British Isles.

> H.A. Baker
> Fruit Officer (retired)
> Royal Horticultural Society

Introduction

It is a long time since there has been a British book published describing pear cultivars, in fact not since Edward Bunyard's "A Handbook of Fruits. Apples and Pears" was published in 1920. That fine book lacked illustrations. The intention now is to provide a companion book for "The Apples of England" by H V Taylor, first published in 1936, Taylor's "Plums of England" published in 1949 and Norman Grubb's "Cherries" also published in 1949, all published by Crosby Lockwood and Son Limited.

In this book fifty five of the more important and best known cultivars grown in Britain are described and illustrated. There are of course many more, with 125 in the collection at the Royal Horticultural Society Garden, Wisley, Surrey and 495 in the National Collection at Brogdale, Faversham, Kent. Most of these are not widely available today, but are all of great historical interest.

The book includes a history of the pear and a section on cultivation. For greater details of cultivation there are excellent books such as The Royal Horticultural Society's "The Fruit Garden Displayed" and "Fruit" by Harry Baker.

Our fifty five varieties are arranged alphabetically and each plate is numbered consecutively with an identifying letter for each cultivar. There is a key facing each plate. There is a plate from a photograph of the pear orchard in blossom at the Brogdale Horticultural Trust.

Pears are delicious fruits and although they have a long history of cultivation in Britain they are not as suited to the British climate as the apple, growing better in the climate of France and Southern Europe where there are warm Springs and long Summers.

Pears have their origins in the Near East including the Caucasus area. They were probably introduced into Britain by the Romans who cultivated a range of fruits in Britain including apples and vines. However the first records of their cultivation are not until after the Norman Conquest. Almost certainly they had been grown during the Dark Ages as they were grown in France at this time and there was contact between the monasteries where much fruit was cultivated. Pears grown on pear rootstocks are very long lived, up to 300 years or more and so they were likely to have survived periods of political and social instability.

The European pear is probably derived from *Pyrus communis* (a native of continental Europe but not Britain), hybridised with other species. *Pyrus communis* is not edible raw (although it can be eaten bletted, when the fruits start to rot on the tree in a similar way to medlars - *Mespilus germanica*) and so it was not until the first natural hybrids arose that pears would have been used for food. These spread to Europe and were cultivated by the Greeks and Romans.

Early pear cultivars tended to be more gritty, lacking the buttery texture of the pears grown today which date mainly from the 18th century onwards.

Pear cultivation spread throughout Britain, including areas considered unsuitable today such as Northern England and Scotland. For instance the area around Jedburgh in Southeast Scotland was known for pear cultivation. This was important before modern transport systems, particularly since pears bruise easily even when unripe. Cultivars suited to local conditions were grown but often lacked the quality of the present commercial cultivars (most of which are 19th century cultivars). One hardy local cultivar still quite widely grown is *Hessle* which probably originated in East Yorkshire.

A number of pears were introduced by Richard Harris, fruiterer to Henry VIII who introduced many fruits including apples, pears and plums and planted them in model orchards at Teynham in Kent. Further pear cultivars were introduced by the Tradescants in the 17th century.

It was in Belgium that the first deliberate hybridisation from selected parents took place. One of the first to carry this out was the Abbé Nicolas Hardenpont (1705-74) of Mons who made deliberate crosses of pears and selected from them. He introduced a number of cultivars and the best of them was *Glou Morceau,* an excellent late pear raised about 1750 but not introduced until about 1820. It has been grown to some extent commercially and is a very good garden cultivar. The monks at Mons had a long history of raising pears. One of the first had been *Doyenné d' Été* around 1700.

Dr Van Mons, a pharmacist and physician of Louvain, Belgium carried out pear breeding in the early to mid 19th century from wild pears and released about 400 cultivars including *Nouveau Poiteau* and *Thompsons*.

Major Pierre Joseph Esperen (1780-1847) of Malines was also raising pears at this time including *Émile d' Heyst* and the very good late pears *Bergamotte Esperen* and *Josephine de Malines*.

Arguably the finest pear raised in the 19th century was raised at the Comice Horticole, Angers, Department of Maine-et-Loire, France and first fruited in 1849. *Doyenné du Comice* is a fine dessert pear widely grown commercially and a good garden cultivar for more favourable sites.

Deliberate pear breeding in Britain started in the early 19th century encouraged by Thomas Andrew Knight, a founder of the Royal Horticultural Society, who carried out controlled pear breeding himself but with little success. However the influence of Knight and the RHS, which set up collection at its gardens at Chiswick (comprising 622 cultivars in 1826 compared with 495 in the Brogdale collection today), did lead to breeding by nurseries and enthusiasts.

The most successful of these was Rivers of Sawbridgeworth. They raised a number of pears, including *Conference* which was exhibited at the National British Pear Conference in 1885 after which it was named. It is the major commercial pear in Britain, widely grown elsewhere and a good garden cultivar. Its origins are in Belgium as it was raised from *Leon Leclerc de Laval* one of Van Mons seedlings. Other pears raised by Rivers include *Fertility, Princess* and *Magnate. Fertility* was grown commercially in the past but is of poor quality.

In the early 20th century Laxton Bros. of Bedford were successful in pear breeding, raising a number of cultivars including *Beurré Bedford, Laxton's Foremost, Laxton's Progress* and *Laxton's Superb*. The best of these was Laxton's Superb (there is also an apple of this name) which is an early pear and a good pollinator for *Doyenné du Comice*. However it proved very susceptible to the disease fireblight, caused by *Erwinia amylovora* which led to its grubbing from orchards to prevent the spread of the disease. It is present in the National Collection at Brogdale and can still be found in some private gardens.

However the most famous British pear cultivar was not a result of controlled breeding. *Williams' Bon Chrétien* originated as a seedling in the garden of schoolmaster Mr Wheeler at Aldermaston, Berkshire. His successor Mr Stair sent grafts to a nurseryman, Richard Williams of Turnham Green, whose name it was given. In the United States it also received a name of a nurseryman 'Bartlett' after Enoch Bartlett. It formed the basis of the Californian canning industry and became the most widely grown cultivar in the world.

Pear breeding continued during the 20th century, with scientific breeding programmes at research stations. At Long Ashton Research Station near Bristol Dr Spinks raised *Bristol Cross* in1931. At the John Innes Research Institute M.B. Crane raised pears including *Merton Pride* in 1941, introduced in 1959, which is an excellent garden cultivar.

Breeding is now carried out at H.R.I. East Malling where Tydeman raised *Beth* in 1938 (named in 1974). *Concorde* was selected in 1977. Further cultivars raised by Dr Frank Alston are under trial. Pear breeding is now carried out by Dr Kate Evans.

Onward, one of the finest garden cultivars, was raised at the National Fruit Trials, Wisley in 1947.

Pear growing spread throughout the world, in particular the USA where many cultivars have been raised but not many are suited to the British climate. So far the only US cultivars planted to any extent are *Clapp's Favourite* raised by Thaddeus Clapp at Dorchester, Massachusetts before 1860 and *Gorham,* raised in 1910 by Richard Wellington at New York State Agricultural Station and introduced in 1923.

Pears are widely grown in the Southern Hemisphere but only *Packham's Triumph* has been widely grown in Britain. This was raised about 1896 by Charles Henry Packham in New South Wales, Australia but did not become widely available until the 1940s.

Modern pear breeding is carried out by only a very few research stations world-wide and concentrates on breeding in resistance to pests and diseases. New selections should require fewer pesticide sprays and so are of great interest to commercial and amateur growers.

It was, however, in the 18th and 19th centuries that the bulk of the fine pears were raised and it is from these pear growers and nurserymen that we have such a wide range today, although this has declined from its heyday. In fact most of the pears grown commercially today were raised in the 18th or 19th century, including *Williams' Bon Chrétien, Doyenné du Comice, Beurré Hardy* and *Conference.*

Some good pears have been raised in the 20th century but so far the 21st century would not appear to hold much promise for many more, although genetic engineering may have its part to play in pears as in other food crops. One of the current interests is in red skinned pears and we should see more of these in the near future. The current commercial cultivars, however, are likely to be grown for some time to come.

Warden Pears

The name *Warden* was probably first given to a pear grown at Warden Abbey in Bedfordshire, but the term "warden" came to signify a type of culinary pear which was much grown in the past.

These pears are very hard and often gritty, they ripen slowly and are never soft enough to be eaten as dessert. They are very long keeping, storing under ordinary storage conditions (in a shed or barn) until April or May.

They take a long time to cook and are baked or stewed slowly with honey or sugar (sugar would not have been available until comparatively recently); spices such as cinnamon or cloves can be added if required. An average cooking time is about two hours. This was more convenient in the days of permanent cooking fires or ranges than today, but they can be poached in a slow cooker or cooked in a pressure cooker for about ten minutes. They were particularly valuable in the days before cold storage, canning, freezing and imports from the Southern hemisphere.

Pears of this type have been grown at least since Roman times and were one of the few fruits or vegetables that could be stored through the winter. Potatoes were not widely cultivated in Northern Europe until the late 17th century and the cucurbits (pumpkins and squashes) not until the 16th century, so warden pears were one of the few foods which lasted through the winter.

The oldest cultivar of this type is *Black Worcester* which may date from Roman times and is posssibly the original warden. Others include the French pears *Catillac* and *Bellisime d'Hiver* and the British *Uvedale's Saint Germain*.

Catillac and *Bellisime d'Hiver* turn pink on cooking. *Catillac* is often considered the best but in recent years I have considered *Black Worcester* to have better flavour. This may be due to the recent succession of hot dry summers.

Although not so relevant to today's needs these pears are still very pleasant when cooked and worth the effort. They are worth including where there is space to grow a number of cultivars. Many old trees still exist as they are generally fairly vigorous and long lived. *Uvedale's Saint Germain* is probably the most vigorous and I have seen an espalier trained tree with over twenty tiers.

Asian Pears

Asian or Nashi pears are distinct from European Pears having been derived from different *Pyrus* species, particularly *Pyrus serotina* and *Pyrus ussuriensis.* These are generally russeted and apple shaped, resembling russet apples. They have a crisp, slightly gritty texture (they are also known as sand pears) and are juicy, but most have little flavour.

Asian pears have been little grown in Britain but there is a selection of twenty cultivars at the RHS Garden, Wisley, and a few are now available including *Chojuro* and *Nijisseiki.* They are grown in the same way as European pears but flower very early with the first European pears, so are more subject to damage by spring frosts and they need a particularly sheltered position. Some cultivars do not grow well and are clearly not suited to British conditions, but once it is clear which are suited best, they should have a limited use for garden cultivation in sheltered areas.

There are hybrids between these and European pears but these are also suited to warmer climates. The oldest of these is *Keiffer* raised by Peter Kieffer at Roxborough near Philadelphia and first fruited in 1863. It was widely grown in the USA in the past but is of poor quality. Since then further hybrids have been raised including *Fan Stil, Maxine* and *Orient.*

When grown under British conditions Asian Pears cannot compare with European Pears for intensity of flavour. They are essentially different, but despite their rather bland taste their crisp texture and juiciness make them a very good addition to a vegetable or fruit salad.

None have been described in this book as they are a separate subject and so far little grown in Britain.

Perry Pears

Perry pears are fairly small and usually quite astringent (although some are suitable to eat or cook).They are crushed and pressed to produce juice used to make perry, in much the same way as cider and wine are produced. The best perry is a fine drink of a quality equal to good wine.

They arose as hybrids between *Pyrus communis* and *Pyrus nivalis* both native to central Europe but not to Britain.

Perry has been produced since ancient times but probably not in Britain until relatively recently. Perry pear cultivars were probably introduced from France following the Norman Conquest although there is no written reference to perry until the 16th century.

Perry pear cultivation has not been widespread in Britain, restricted mainly to neighbouring areas of Gloucestershire, Herefordshire and Worcestershire, although more recently they have been cultivated in Somerset. In these areas they were cultivated on the heavier clay soils on which pears will grow well but on which apple cultivation is not so successful.

Perry pear cultivation reached a peak in the late 17th and early 18th century and has declined since then, although many trees from this time are still in existence. They are often of great size characterizing the landscape of the perry producing areas.

Perry pear cultivars are a subject in themselves and so are not described in this book. Appendix I lists the cultivars recognised as Perry Pears by the Ministry of Agriculture Fisheries and Food in 1989 when the Apple and Pear Development Council was established and acreages of perry pears were exempt from the levy.

Pear Cultivation

Pears flower early (generally during April) and many also require a long season to ripen fully. Because of this they grow and fruit best in a site sheltered from strong winds, sunny and free from spring frosts. A gentle south, south-west or west facing slope is ideal.

As altitude increases, strength of wind increases and temperature decreases so generally pear cultivation is not advised above an altitude of about 150 m (500ft). However this applies mainly to commercial orchards; pears can be grown at higher altitudes providing that a sheltered site, suitable cultivars and training forms are chosen. By training pears as cordons, espaliers or fans against warm south, south-west or west facing walls or fences, they can be grown satisfactorily in Northern locations and at altitude.

Pears grow best on deep, well drained, moisture retentive soils with a pH around 6-7. They can be grown on a wide range of soils, they are generally more successful on wetter soils rather than dry soils. It is important on light dry soils to improve moisture retention by incorporating plenty of organic matter before planting and by regular mulching with organic matter such as well rotted manure or compost.

Pears are grafted or budded onto rootstocks. In the past pears were usually grafted onto pear seedlings. These are vigorous, however, producing very large trees, sometimes 12 m (40 ft) in height, and are slow to come into bearing, making them generally unsuitable for modern commercial or garden cultivation. Today the most widely used rootstocks are clonal Quince (*Cydonia oblonga*) rootstocks. Of these Quince A and Quince C are the most common. There is not much difference in vigour between them; Quince A is moderately vigorous and Quince C is semi-dwarfing. Pears grafted onto Quince come into fruiting early in the life of the tree (often in the second or third year after planting) and produce good quality fruit. Not all pears are compatible with Quince rootstocks and incompatible cultivars have to be "double worked", that is a compatible cultivar has to be grafted on first as an interstock. Cultivars used as interstocks include *Beurré Hardy, Doyenné du Comice* and *Fertility*. Cultivars requiring double working include *Beurré Clairgeau, Bristol Cross, Clapp's Favourite, Dr Jules Guyot, Doyenné d'Été, Forelle, Jargonelle, Marguerite Marillat, Marie Louise, Merton Pride, Packham's Triumph, Souvenir du Congrès* and *Williams' Bon Chrétien* (most clones). If uncertain about the compatibility of a cultivar use an interstock.

Tree forms.

Pears are suited to a range of tree forms. In sheltered locations and where space allows they can be grown as open centred bush trees on Quince A rootstock. These have a clear stem of about 75 cm (30 in) before the branches start and should be spaced about 4.5 m (15 ft) apart.

Modern commercial pear orchards in Britain mainly consist of closely planted spindlebush trees. They are a form of centre leader, cone shaped tree. They are grown on Quince A or C rootstock depending on site and spacing.

Restrictive Trained Forms.

For small gardens and in less favourable locations pears are best grown as trained forms such as oblique cordons, espaliers and fans. They can be grown against warm south, south-west or west facing walls or fences, or on freestanding posts and wires.

Cordons consist of a single stem and take up the least space. They are spaced about 75 cm (2 ft 6 in) apart. Quince C is generally the best rootstock but Quince A can be used for weak growing cultivars such as *Doyenné d'Été* or on poor soils.

Espaliers consist of a central stem and a number of horizontal tiers of branches, commonly 3 or 4. Quince A or C can be used depending on the size required.

Fan trained trees consist of a number of branches trained out in a fan shape and can also be grown on Quince A or C depending on the size required.

Pears can also be grown in restricted forms as pyramids on Quince A or C. They are useful as freestanding trees in a small garden with sunlight reaching all parts of the tree and they cast little shade.

All the restricted forms, cordons, espaliers and pyramids, are summer pruned, on the modified Lorette system since the growth slows down usually in early August in the south of England (later in the further north and west). Pruning at this time restricts growth and encourages fruit bud development near the base of the shoots.

Pears can be grown in a range of trained forms and good examples of these can be seen at the Hatton Fruit Garden at H.R.I. East Malling (rarely open to the public) and the Potager de Roi at Versailles in France (regularly open to the public).

Recommended Cultivars
in season order

Dessert:

    Jargonelle
    Beth
    Précoce de Trévoux
    Williams' Bon Chrétien
    Merton Pride
    Fondante D'Automne
    Onward
    Beurré Hardy
    Louise Bonne of Jersey
    Pitmaston Duchess
    Conference
    Concorde
    Émile d'Heyst
    Doyenné du Comice
    Nouveau Poiteau
    Glou Morceau
    Josephine de Malines
    Oliver de Serres

Culinary:

    Catillac

Recommended Cultivars for Northern or other cooler locations

Dessert:

Jargonelle
Beth
Dr Jules Guyot
Beurré d'Amanlis
Onward
Beurré Hardy
Hessle
Louise Bonne of Jersey
Pitmaston Duchess
Conference
Émile d'Heyst
Nouveau Poiteau

Culinary:

Catillac

Picking and Storing Pears

Timing of picking is very important. If pears are picked too early they will shrivel in storage; if picked too late they tend to rot from the core while still on the tree.

Exact timing of picking each cultivar varies from season to season and according to location. As the pear approaches maturity there will be a slight colour change to a lighter shade of green. If the pear is lifted in the palm of the hand and twisted slightly it should part easily from the spur. The final test is to bite into it. If it is hard but sweet it is ready to pick; if it is hard and starchy it should be left a little longer. This is particularly important for early and mid-season pears. Late season pears do not usually rot on the tree and will drop if left too long.

Once picked they should be stored in a cool dark place, ideally laid out in flat trays so that they can be inspected easily. When nearly ripe they should start to turn yellow (except for a few cultivars which remain green, including *Beurré d'Amanlis*) and should then be moved a few at a time to room temperature to complete ripening.

Pears can be stored at lower temperatures than apples, 0 to +1 C (32 to 34 F), and although this is rarely achieved in home storage, they can be stored in places too cold for apples, such as many sheds and garages. Small quantities can be stored in a refrigerator providing the temperature does not drop below zero.

Pollination

Pears are generally self-sterile, that is they will only produce fruit if pollinated with pollen from another compatible cultivar flowering at the same time. Most pears are compatible with others flowering at the same time but a few are not, including the following groups which will not pollinate others within the group:

1. *Fondante d'Automne, Louise Bonne of Jersey, Précoce de Trévoux, Seckle, Williams' Bon Chrétien.*

2. *Beurré d'Amanlis, Conference.*

3. *Onward, Doyenné du Comice.*

Most pears are diploid but some are triploid (marked with T). Triploid cultivars are not effective as pollinators, so when a triploid is grown two other diploid culltivars must be grown to pollinate the triploid and each other. There are some tetraploid sports of cultivars including *Improved Fertility* (a sport of *Fertility*) and *Double Williams' a sport of Williams' Bon Chrétien*). Some cultivars are male sterile (marked MS) and so ineffective as pollinators in the same way as triploid cultivars.

For ease of choosing suitable pollinators they can be divided into four groups. When choosing pears to plant, pollinators should be from within the same group or adjacent groups.

Pollination Group A

Précoce de Trévoux

Pollination Group B

Bellisime d'Hiver
Beurré d'Amanlis (T)
Beurré d'Anjou
Beurré Clairgeau
Beurré Diel (T)
Doyenné d'Été
Émile d'Heyst
Forelle
Le Brun
Louise Bonne of Jersey
Marguerite Marillat (MS)
Packham's Triumph
Passe Crasanne
Princess
Uvedale's St Germain (T)
Vicar of Winkfield (T)

Pollination Group C

Bergamotte d'Automne
Bergamotte d'Esperen
Beurré Hardy
Beurré Superfin
Black Worcester
Concorde
Conference
Doyenné Boussoch (T)
Dr Jules Guyot
Durondeau
Fertility
Fondante d'Automne
Hessle
Jargonelle (T)
Josephine de Malines
Marie Louise d'Uccle
Merton Pride (T)
Olivier de Serres
Souvenir du Congrès
Thompsons
Williams' Bon Chrétien

Pollination Group D

Beth
Beurré Bedford (MS)
Bristol Cross (MS)
Catillac (T)
Clapp's Favourite
Doyenné Blanc
Doyenné du Comice
Glou Morceau
Gorham
Improved Fertility
Laxton's Foremost
Marie Louise
Michaelmas Nelis
Nouveau Poiteau
Onward
Pitmaston Duchess (T)
Winter Nelis

Description and Identification of Pears

Describing and identifying any type of fruit is not easy. Pears are particularly difficult because many of the characters used to describe them vary within each cultivar, between fruits on one tree from site to site and from year to year. I have mentioned in the descriptions when cultivars are particularly variable in any respect, but they will all vary to some extent. In order to standardise the descriptions I have used the following titles:

Picking time
Season for use
Colour
Skin
Shape
Stalk
Cavity
Eye
Basin
Size
Flesh
Weight
Leaves

The following terms are also used:

Lenticels - pores on the surface of the fruit often conspicuous as medium or large dots.

Sepals - constitute the main part of the eye and are remnants of the flower.

Stamens - also remnants of the flower, not always present.

Leaves - leaves margins serrate: with sharp toothed margin;

    - leaves margins crenate: with rounded indentations to margin;

    - leaves margins entire: without indentation.

Shape - see diagrams on next page.

stalk
stalk cavity

eye basin   eye

Pear Shapes

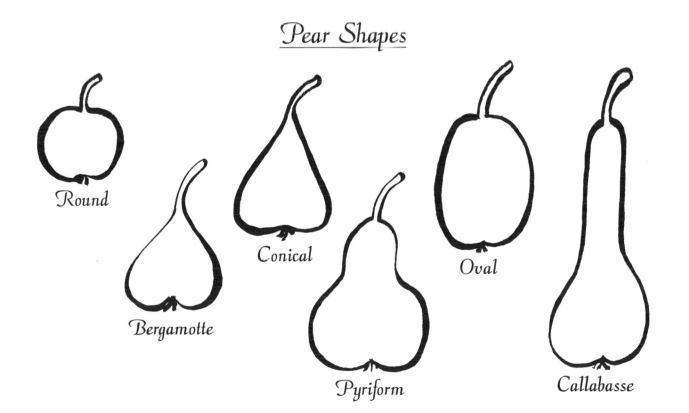

Round

Bergamotte

Conical

Pyriform

Oval

Callabasse

When identifying pears it is always important to compare at least three fruits of each cultivar, as characters vary, shape in particular. The fruits should be mature and typical of that cultivar, of an average size for the cultivar and complete with stalks. Small fruits produced from late flowers are atypical and not possible to identify.

As with all identification it is always best to eliminate the obvious cultivars first. It is far more likely to be a common pear such as *Conference, Williams' Bon Chrétien, Doyenné du Comice* or *Beurré Hardy* than a less common cultivar.

Leaves are an important aid to identification and I have measured the petiole length as this appears to be more constant than the actual leaf dimensions.

Plates

Plate I

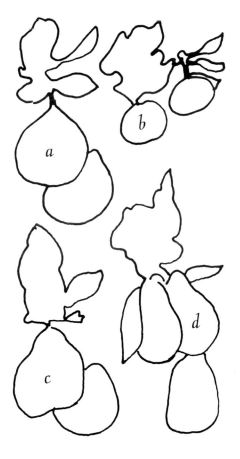

a. Bellisime d'hiver

b. Bergamotte d'Automne

c. Bergamotte Esperen

d. Beth

Sally Pinhey

Plate 5

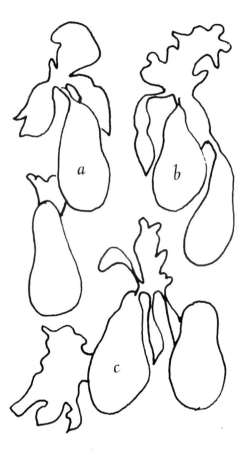

a. Concorde

b. Conference

c. Dr Jules Guyot

Sally Pinhey

Plate 6

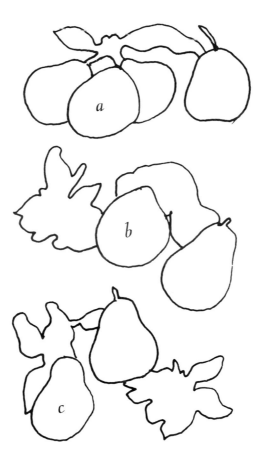

a. Doyenné Blanc
b. Doyenné Bussoch
c. Doyenné du Comice

Sally Pinhey

Plate 7

a. Doyenné d'Été

b. Durondeau

c. Émile d'Heyst

d. Fertility

Sally Pinhey

Plate 8

a. Fondante d'Antomne
b. Forelle
c. Glou Morceau
d. Gorham

Sally Pinhey

Plate 9

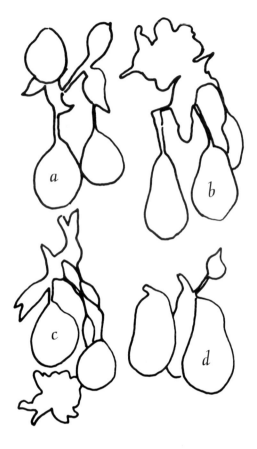

a. Hessle
b. Jargonelle
c. Josephine de Malines
d. Laxton's Foremost

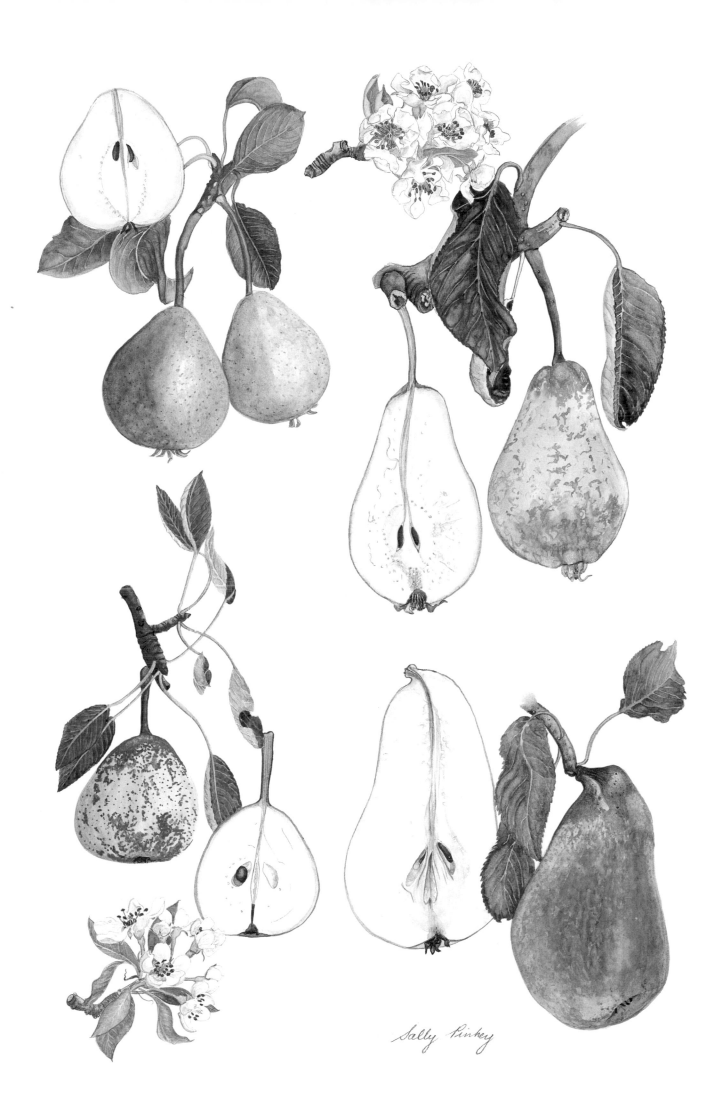

Sally Pinhey

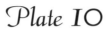

Plate 10

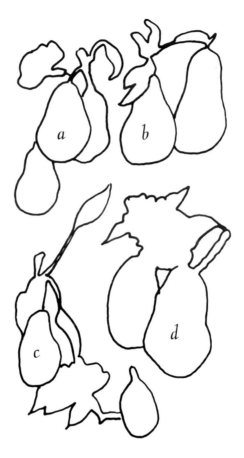

a. Jules d'Airolles
b. Le Brun
c. Louise Bonne of Jersey
d. Marguerite Marillat

Sally Pinhey

Plate II

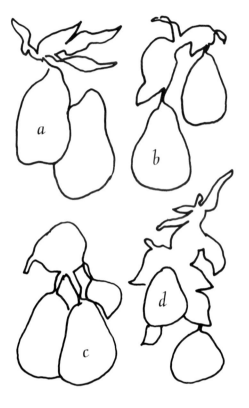

a. Marie Louise
b. Marie Louis d'Uccle
c. Merton Pride
d. Michaelmas Nelis

Sally Pinhey

Plate 12

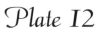

a. Nouveau Poiteau

b. Olivier de Serres

c. Onward

d. Packham's Triumph

Sally Pinkey

Plate 13

a. Passe Crassane

b. Pitmaston Duchess

c. Précoce de Trévoux

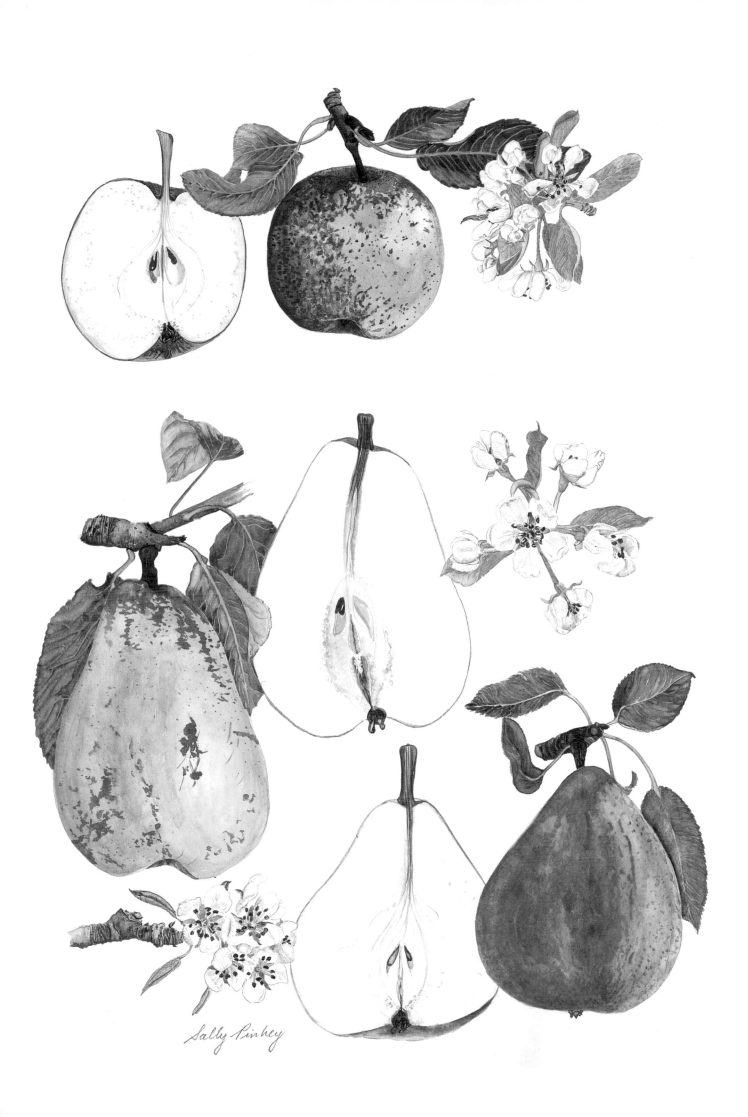

Sally Pinhey

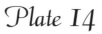

Plate 14

a. Princess

b. Souvenir de Congrèss

c. Thompsons

d. Uvedale St Germain

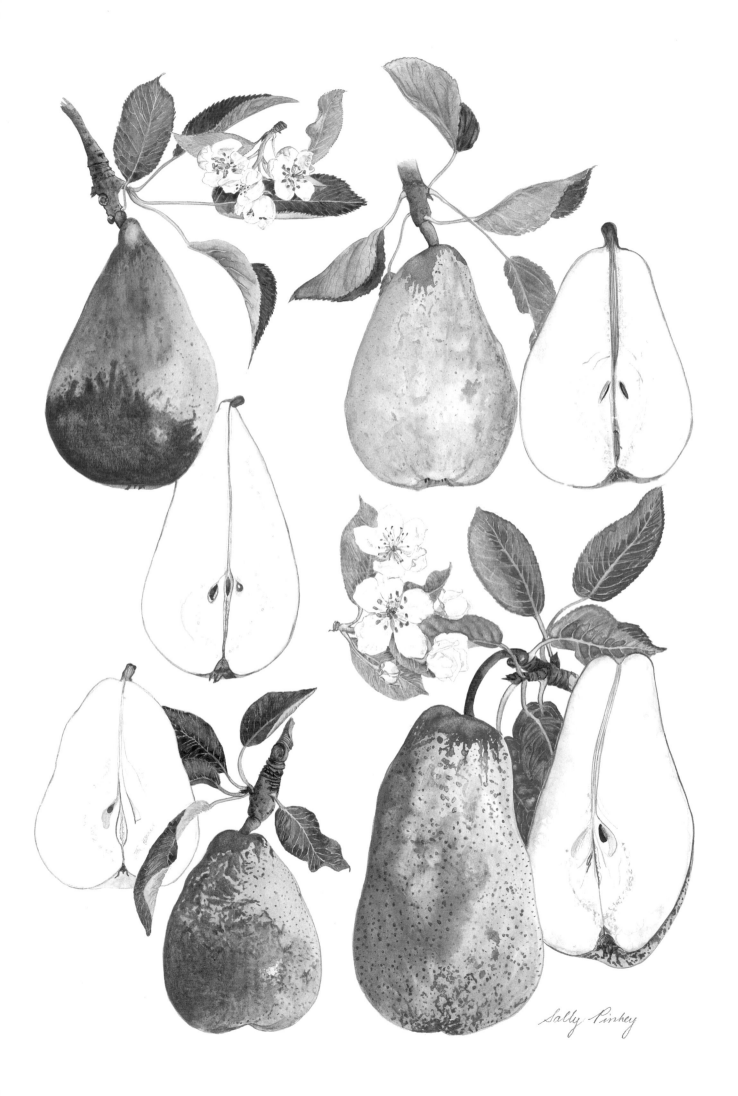

Sally Pinkey

Plate 15

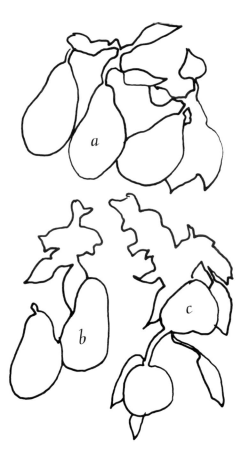

a. Vicar of Winkfield

b. Williams' Bon Chrétien

c. Winter Nelis

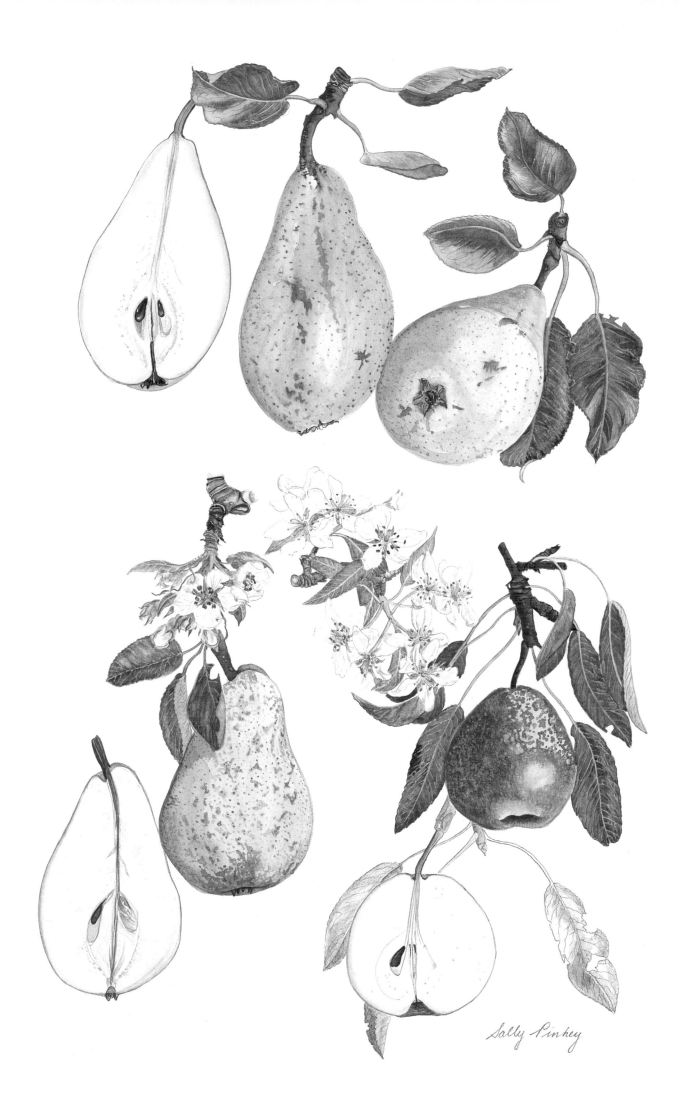

Sally Pinhey

Pear orchard in blossom   Brogdale Horticultural Trust, Faversham, Kent

Plate 1
Fruit A

NAME	*Bellisime d'Hiver*
HISTORY	A very old French cultivar of uncertain origin but first described in 1768. One of the best culinary pears. Tree growth is upright and fairly compact. Pears need cooking slowly for 1-2 hours after which time they turn pink.
PICKING TIME	Late October.
SEASON	January to March.
COLOUR	Dull Green changing to yellowish green. Some Fruits 1/4 to 1/2 flushed with pinkish red, with some indistinct stripes. Not much russet but sometimes some brown russet around the eye. Lenticels conspicuous as small green or russet dots.
SKIN	Smooth.
SHAPE	Short conical to oval.
STALK	Medium length, 24 mm, medium thickness, inserted at an angle.
CAVITY	Shallow.
EYE	Medium, open, sepals separated at base, upright with tips reflexed. Stamens present.
BASIN	Shallow.
SIZE	Medium to large, 71 mm wide, 74 mm long.
FLESH	White, fairly fine, gritty at the core, some flavour when uncooked.
WEIGHT	200 g.
LEAVES	Oval, shallow crenate. Petiole 30 mm long.

Plate 1
Fruit B

NAME	*Bergamotte d'Automne*
HISTORY	Its origin is uncertain but one of the oldest pears in cultivation, in existence in the middle ages and possibly dating from Roman times, originating in Italy or Asia. It makes a compact tree and crops regularly, the fruit is of good quality and still worthy of garden cultivation.
PICKING TIME	Mid September.
SEASON	October - November.
COLOUR	Dull green changing to yellowish green, some fruits with red flush over about half of the surface. Fruits are heavily russeted with golden or brown russet coarsely netted.
SKIN	Rough.
SHAPE	Flat to round, rarely bergamotte, apple like.
STALK	Short, 12 mm, variable and thick, generally inserted upright.
CAVITY	Medium depth and narrow.
EYE	Small, open, sepals fused at base and sometimes reflexed.
BASIN	Medium width and depth.
SIZE	Small, 52 mm wide, 41 mm long (sometimes a little larger).
FLESH	White, melting, moderately juicy with a rich aromatic flavour.
WEIGHT	60 g.
LEAVES	Small, oval, pointed, twisted, entire. Petiole long, 40 mm or more.

Plate 1
Fruit C

NAME	*Bergamotte Esperen*
HISTORY	Raised by Major Esperen at Malines, Belgium about 1830. It is a high quality late pear best grown against a warm wall or fence in order to ripen well and crop reliably.
PICKING TIME	Late October.
SEASON	February to end of March.
COLOUR	Dull mottled green turning to yellowish green with patches of brown russet particularly at the stalk and eye. Lenticels conspicuous as large russet dots.
SKIN	Rough.
SHAPE	Variable bergamotte to round conical, slightly uneven.
STALK	Short and thick, sometimes only 8 mm long, often obliquely inserted.
CAVITY	Narrow and shallow.
EYE	Closed or half open, sepals fused at base and pressed in.
BASIN	Moderately deep and narrow.
SIZE	Medium, 65 mm wide, 65 mm long or slightly larger.
FLESH	Yellowish white, juicy, melting, perfumed, slightly gritty at core. Very good flavour particularly after a warm summer.
WEIGHT	140 g.
LEAVES	Long, oval, upfolded, shallow serrate, petiole 28 mm.

Plate 1
Fruit D

NAME	*Beth*
HISTORY	Raised in 1938 by H.M. Tydeman at East Malling Research Station (H.R.I. East Malling) from *Beurré Superfin* x *Williams' Bon Chrétien*. Recommended for release in 1969 and named in 1974. Compact, reliable and heavy cropping with pleasant flavour. A good garden cultivar.
PICKING TIME	Late August to early September.
SEASON	Early to mid September.
COLOUR	Pale green turning to pale yellow with sometimes very faint orange pink flush. Variable amounts of russet with russet around stalk and other small spots and patches of russet, but some fruits almost clean. Lenticels small but conspicuous as green or brown russet dots.
SKIN	Smooth.
SHAPE	Conical to short conical, variable with some fruits pyriform.
STALK	Short, 23 mm, thick, some inserted upright, others obliquely.
CAVITY	Shallow.
EYE	Small, closed or partly open. Sepals convergent, clasping with tips pressed in. Fleshy at base and fused.
BASIN	Shallow.
SIZE	Small to medium, 55 mm wide, 70 mm long.
FLESH	Creamy white, juicy, melting, sweet, good flavour.
WEIGHT	120 g.
LEAVES	Fairly large, round to oval, coarsely crenate. Petiole 30 mm.

Plate 2
Fruit A

NAME	*Beurré d'Amanlis* Synonyms include: *Hubard, Wilhelmine, Delbart.*
HISTORY	Origin uncertain, probably raised at Amanlis near Rennes, France before 1800 and introduced in 1826. Widely grown in the past, reliable and apparently hardy, but there are now better cultivars available at this season (including *Merton Pride* and *Onward*). It is a triploid cultivar.
PICKING TIME	Early September.
SEASON	September.
COLOUR	Dull pea green changing only slightly when ripe to yellowish green (the colour change is difficult to detect). Occasionally slight reddish flush. Russet particularly around eye, some fruits three quarters covered by thin continuous russet. Lenticels fairly inconspicuous as medium russet dots.
SKIN	Rough.
SHAPE	Round pyriform, fairly even.
STALK	Medium length and thickness, inserted upright or at slight angle, some with wrinkle at base.
CAVITY	Medium.
EYE	Closed or half open. Sepals fused at base, some appear pressed in. Stamens present.
BASIN	Fairly wide and very shallow.
SIZE	Medium, 67 mm wide, 63 mm long.
FLESH	Pale yellow, fairly juicy, slightly gritty and gritty at core, pleasant mild flavour.
WEIGHT	150 g.
LEAVES	Round oval or oval, some pointed, sharply serrate. Dark green.

Plate 2
Fruit B

NAME	*Beurré d'Anjou*
HISTORY	The origin and naming of *Beurré d'Anjou* is uncertain. It probably originated in the Angers area of France. It was introduced into Britain by Thomas Rivers early in the 19th century. It has been grown commercially particularly in the USA where a red clone *Red Anjou* is also grown. Tree growth is weak and compact and it does not ripen well in Britain, but fruit size is always good.
PICKING TIME	Late October.
SEASON	Late November - January.
COLOUR	Pale green turning pale yellow, slight pink flush on some fruits,variable netting of brown russet patches and dots with a russet patch around stalk an eye. Lenticels conspicuous as small or medium russet dots.
SKIN	Smooth.
SHAPE	Round oval. Asymmetrical with stalk obliquely inserted.
STALK	Short and thick, 7 mm.
CAVITY	Shallow and fairly narrow, appears as a slight depression.
EYE	Small, open, sepals flattened.
BASIN	Medium to shallow.
SIZE	Large, 73 mm wide, 80 mm long. Size consistent even on small or stunted trees.
FLESH	Yellowish white, fairly juicy, slightly granular, flavour mild in Britain, better when grown in warmer climate areas.
WEIGHT	240 g.
LEAVES	Oval, upfolded, entire or slightly crenate, petiole 32 mm.

Plate 2
Fruit C

NAME	*Beurré Bedford*
HISTORY	Raised in 1902 by Laxton Bros at Bedford from *Marie-Louise* x *Durondeau,* introduced in 1921. A fair quality pear of moderate cropping, one of a number of cultivars raised by Laxton Bros.
PICKING TIME	Mid - late September.
SEASON	October.
COLOUR	Light green becoming pale yellow often with bright pink flush over up to half of suface, some indistinct stripes. Variable amount of russet from none up to about half covered with small or large patches and sometimes band around fruit. Lenticels conspicuous as green, russet or pink dots.
SKIN	Smooth.
SHAPE	Conical to pyriform, bumpy, tapering towards stem and eye.
STALK	Long, 40 mm, medium thickness, slight bump to one side of stalk.
CAVITY	Shallow with slight bump to one side of stalk.
EYE	Small to medium, sepals fleshy, erect, separated at base. Stamens present.
BASIN	Medium.
SIZE	Medium large, 68 mm wide, 95 mm long.
FLESH	White, coarse, juicy, sweet, quite good, slightly aromatic flavour.
WEIGHT	210 g.
LEAVES	Petiole long 40 mm. Long, oval to lanceolate, entire.

Plate 2
Fruit D

NAME	*Beurré Clairgeau*
HISTORY	Raised about 1830 by Pierre Clairgeau, Nantes, France and fruit first exhibited in 1848. Tree growth is erect and compact. It crops heavily and very reliably. Unfortunately it is generally of poor quality under British conditions and not worth planting although it was fairly widely planted in the past.
PICKING TIME	Early October.
SEASON	Late October - November. Culinary.
COLOUR	Golden brown turning yellow, often orange-red flush over quarter to half of surface. Variable brown russet over much of surface, commonly 3/4. Lenticels conspicuous as brown or black russet dots.
SKIN	Rough.
SHAPE	Conical, some fruit bumpy uneven.
STALK	Short to medium, 8-25 mm, inserted on level, some inserted upright and some at an angle beneath a fleshy bump.
CAVITY	None.
EYE	Large, open, flattened star-like sepals fused at base, stamens present.
BASIN	Shallow.
SIZE	Medium to large, 60 mm wide, 100 mm long.
FLESH	White, gritty especially near core, firm, not very juicy with musky flavour.
WEIGHT	170 g.
LEAVES	Round oval, variable, fine to medium serrate. Petiole long 40 mm.

Plate 3
Fruit A

NAME	***Beurré Diel*** Synonyms: *Diels Butterbirne, Belle Magnifique, Beurré des Trois, Tours.*
HISTORY	It was found at the Chateau of Perck near Vilvoorde, Belgium about 1800 by Meuris, Head Gardener to Van Mons and named after the German pomologist Diel. It was sent to the London Horticultural Society (now the RHS) in 1817. A reliable pear, but needs a good site and a good summer to ripen well.
PICKING TIME	Late September to early October.
SEASON	October/November.
COLOUR	Dull green changing to dull yellowish green, sometimes slight brownish flush. Russet as small patches and large dots over most of fruit. Lenticels fairly inconspicuous as small russet dots.
SKIN	Slightly rough.
SHAPE	Round to oval often with flattened sides.
STALK	Medium to long, 27 mm, curved. Inserted upright, fleshy at base.
CAVITY	Very shallow.
EYE	Open. Sepals quite long, erect and fused at base. Stamens present.
BASIN	Narrow and quite deep.
SIZE	Medium, 72 mm wide, 70 mm long.
FLESH	Creamy white, juicy, melting, fine, slightly gritty at core. Excellent fine flavour.
WEIGHT	190 g.
LEAVES	Oval, pointed, crenate. Petiole short, 18 mm.

Plate 3
Fruit B

NAME	*Beurré Hardy* Synonyms including *Beurré Gellert.*
HISTORY	Raised about 1820 by M. Bonnet in Boulogne, France. In 1830 it was acquired by M. Jamin, a nurseryman and named after M. Hardy, Director and Professor of Arboriculture at the Luxembourg Gardens. It was introduced to Britain about 1840. A reliable good cropping, good quality pear. It makes a vigorous and upright tree. It is grown commercially on the Continent and on a small scale in Britain. One of the best garden cultivars.
PICKING TIME	Mid September.
SEASON	October.
COLOUR	Light green, most fruits almost covered with bronze russet, red flush on some fruits over quarter to half of surface. Lenticels fairly conspicuous as small to large russet dots, which are sunken giving a slightly hammered surface.
SKIN	Rough.
SHAPE	Round conical and a few fruits pyriform.
STALK	Short, 14 mm, thick but variable, often inserted at a slight angle.
CAVITY	Shallow.
EYE	Large, open, sepals erect, divided at base with some tips reflexed. Stamens often present.
BASIN	Moderately wide and shallow to moderately deep.
SIZE	Medium to large (often larger than samples described), 68 mm wide, 76 mm long.
FLESH	Creamy (green under skin). Fine, juicy, tender with rose water flavour.
WEIGHT	180 g, but often greater.
LEAVES	Large, round, almost entire, dark green with good autumn colour turning orange red.

Plate 3
Fruit C

NAME	*Beurré Superfin*
HISTORY	Raised in 1837 by M. Goubault at Mille Pieds near Angers, France and first fruited in 1844. A high quality pear which grows well, but does not crop well on all sites. Certainly well worth growing on warm sheltered sites.
PICKING TIME	Mid - late September
SEASON	October.
COLOUR	Mid green turning yellow, numerous patches of light brown russet over most of fruit, some fruits completely russetted. Lenticels fairly inconspicuous as green or russet dots.
SKIN	Rough.
SHAPE	Round to round conical.
STALK	Short to medium and stout, 25 mm long, inserted upright or at slight angle on level, continued with one or two fleshy wrinkles at the base.
CAVITY	None or shallow, depression on one side if stalk at an angle.
EYE	Small, generally open. Short star like sepals with tips often broken off and fused at base.
BASIN	Round, moderately wide and moderate to deep.
SIZE	Medium, 67 mm wide, 67 mm long.
FLESH	Pale yellow, fine, melting, slightly gritty at core. Delicious scented flavour.
WEIGHT	180 g.
LEAVES	Oval, upcupped, irregularly crenate.

Plate 3
Fruit D

NAME	*Black Worcester*
HISTORY	Origin uncertain, but one of the oldest pears in cultivation. It appears on the coat of arms of Worcester and was grown there before 1575 when Queen Elizabeth I saw it at Whystone Farm. It is possibly the same as the French cultivar *de Livre* and may even date from Roman times. Tree growth vigorous spreading, reliable and heavy cropping. It never softens to eat for dessert and needs cooking slowly for 1-2 hours. It is seldom planted today but many old trees still exist.
PICKING TIME	Late October to early November.
SEASON	January to April.
COLOUR	Dull green, almost entirely covered by brown russet. Many fruits have a purplish flush which through the russet often gives a black appearance. Lenticels inconspicuous as small to medium russet dots.
SKIN	Rough.
SHAPE	Oval to pyriform, irregular.
STALK	Short, 15 mm, medium thickness, inserted upright.
CAVITY	Medium to shallow, sometimes with bump within cavity.
EYE	Open or half open. Sepals separated at base, upright, some with tips reflexed. Stamens present.
BASIN	Variable, shallow to deep.
SIZE	Large, 78 mm wide, 85 mm long.
FLESH	Cream, tinged green under the skin. Crisp, coarse, gritty particularly around core. Fairly juicy, little flavour uncooked, but not flavourless.
WEIGHT	260 g.
LEAVES	Oval, slightly serrate, almost entire. Petiole 24 mm.

Plate 4
Fruit A

NAME	*Bristol Cross*
HISTORY	Raised in 1920 by G.T. Spinks at Long Ashton Research Station in Bristol from *Williams Bon Chrétien* x *Conference*. Introduced in 1931. A heavy cropping pear of good quality on heavy soils. It was grown commercially on a small scale for a while but season overlaps with *Conference* which is a superior pear. Since it produces little viable pollen is useless as a pollinator.
PICKING TIME	Mid September.
SEASON	Late September to early October.
COLOUR	Yellowish green becoming pale yellow. Many fruits nearly covered with solid or mottled green or brown russet but some almost clean. Occasional flush over about a quarter of the surface. Lenticels inconspicuous small russet dots.
SKIN	Rough but smooth if russet free.
SHAPE	Oval pyriform to calabasse, slightly uneven.
STALK	Short, 12mm, medium thickness, some stalks upright, some inserted at an angle.
CAVITY	Slight, very shallow.
EYE	Medium open, sepals upright with tips convergent, separated at base.
BASIN	None, eye on the level.
SIZE	Medium, 65 mm wide, 90 mm long.
FLESH	Yellowish white, fine, gritty, particularly around the core, juicy, sweet, excellent flavour.
WEIGHT	170 g.
LEAVES	Long, oval to lanceolate. Petiole 34 mm . Bright red autumn colour.

Plate 4
Fruit B

NAME	*Catillac*
HISTORY	Origin uncertain, first recorded in 1665 and one of the oldest in cultivation, probably found in Cadillac in the Gironde, France. Growth vigorous and spreading, heavy cropping and fairly reliable (it is a triploid). *Catillac* is a culinary pear requiring cooking slowly for a long time (1-2 hours typically), after which time it is pleasant and turning pale pink. Pears of this type were very useful in the past and many old trees are still in existence. Probably the best of the cooking pears.
PICKING TIME	Mid October.
SEASON	January - April.
COLOUR	Dull green changing to greenish yellow. Some fruits with dull red flush over up to three quarters of fruit, with some indistinct stripes. Variable russet, most fruits almost clean with occasional russet patch or dots. Lenticels conspicuous as small russet dots.
SKIN	Smooth.
SHAPE	Bergamotte, slightly bumpy.
STALK	Medium length, 28 mm, thick, slightly curved, inserted upright or at a slight angle, fleshy towards base.
CAVITY	Medium and slightly ribbed.
EYE	Open. Sepals upright, separated at base with tips reflexed. Stamens present.
BASIN	Medium to large with wavy hair lines present in and around some.
SIZE	Large, 92 mm wide, 88 mm long.
FLESH	White, greenish white under the skin, hard, coarse and gritty particularly near core. Suitable for cooking only.
WEIGHT	350 g.
LEAVES	Large, round to round oval, pointed, shallow serrate. Petiole 30 mm long.

Plate 4
Fruit C

NAME	*Clapp's Favourite*
HISTORY	Raised by Thaddeus Clapp, Dorchester, Massachusetts, date uncertain, but before 1860. One of the better early pears of fair flavour preceding *Williams Bon Chrétien*. It has been grown commercially in USA and other countries including Britain in the past. Tree growth is moderate with a drooping habit. Picking timing is important as it is prone to rot from the core.
PICKING TIME	Late August.
SEASON	Mid - late August.
COLOUR	Pale green changing to pale yellow, most fruits about half flushed with bright scarlet with some stipes. Not much russet, small russet patch spreading from stalk and sometimes other russet patches. Lenticels conspicuous as green or red dots.
SKIN	Smooth and faintly hammered.
SHAPE	Pyriform, tapering slightly towards eye.
STALK	Medium, 22 mm, very thick, inserted obliquely.
CAVITY	Slight.
EYE	Closed or slightly open, medium. Sepals fleshy, fused at base, erect with tips reflexed.
BASIN	Medium, even.
SIZE	Medium, 68 mm wide, 87 mm long.
FLESH	Pale yellow, juicy, gritty towards core, little flavour.
WEIGHT	170 g.
LEAVES	Long oval, finely serrate. Petiole 50 mm.

Plate 5
Fruit A

NAME	*Concorde*
HISTORY	Raised at HRI East Malling from *Doyenné du Comice* x *Conference* and selected in 1977. *Concorde* makes a compact tree and fruits very heavily. It is very suitable for cordon training and a good garden cultivar. It is grown commercially in Britain as well as in other countries.
PICKING TIME	End of September.
SEASON	October/November.
COLOUR	Pale green turning yellow, some fruits with large amounts of golden or brown russet in patches and dots, other fruits with very little russet. Some fruits on some sites are flushed orange red with broad indistinct stripes. Lenticels inconspicuous as small russet dots.
SKIN	Smooth to rough depending on amount of russet present.
SHAPE	Pyriform to calabasse, variable, some fruits bumpy and bossed.
STALK	Medium to long, 20 -35 mm, medium thickness, often curved, inserted upright or at a slight angle.
CAVITY	Shallow, some fruits with a fleshy bump to one side.
EYE	Medium open, sepals erect or flattened, starlike, fused at base and sometimes fleshy.
BASIN	Very shallow to medium.
SIZE	Medium to large, 68 mm wide, 115 mm long.
FLESH	Pale yellow, sweet, juicy, melting, buttery, fine texture with pleasant mild flavour.
WEIGHT	220 g.
LEAVES	Round oval to oval, pointed. Very shallow crenate, almost entire. Petiole generally 40 mm, but variable.

Plate 5
Fruit B

NAME	*Conference*
HISTORY	Raised by Rivers of Sawbridgeworth from *Leon Leclerc de Laval* open pollinated and exhibited at the National British Pear Conference of 1885 hence its name. It is the best of several pears raised by Rivers and the best all round pear for cultivation in Britain. It is reliable, heavy cropping and will produce parthenocarpic fruit when grown without a pollinator. The flavour is consistently good if not quite the finest. It is the most widely commercially grown pear in Britain and also widely grown on the Continent.
PICKING TIME	End of September.
SEASON	October/November.
COLOUR	Yellowish green. A lot of brown russet often continuous over areas of the fruit. Some fruits almost clean, others almost entirely russetted with variation according to site and weather. Occasionally pink flushed on chalky soils. Lenticels conspicuous as large russet dots.
SKIN	Slightly rough.
SHAPE	Most fruits pyriform to calabasse, even. Some parthenocarpic fruits are distorted and banana shaped.
STALK	Medium to long, woody, curved, inserted centrally.
CAVITY	Slight cavity or almost continued.
EYE	Medium open sepals, upright and fused at base. Stamens present.
BASIN	Shallow.
SIZE	Medium, 70 mm wide, 120 mm long.
FLESH	Pale yellow with slight pinkish tinge towards the core. Melting, very juicy and sweet with pleasant pear flavour.
WEIGHT	200 g, but can be less if fruits are not thinned.
LEAVES	Fairly large, round oval, irregularly serrate. Petiole 38 mm.

Plate 5
Fruit C

NAME	*Dr Jules Guyot*
HISTORY	Raised by M. Ernest Baltet of Troyes, France in 1870. Reliable and heavy cropping almost every year. Tree growth is moderate and upright. It is similar but inferior to *Williams Bon Chrétien* with little flavour. It was widely grown for market in the past but little grown today.
PICKING TIME	Late August to early September.
SEASON	Early to mid September.
COLOUR	Pale green turning to pale yellow, some fruits with light orange flush and some faint stripes over quarter to half of surface. Variable russet, some fruits almost clean, others with russet spreading from stalk and around the eye. Lenticels fairly small but conspicuous as green or brown dots.
SKIN	Smooth.
SHAPE	Pyriform and slightly bumpy, uneven.
STALK	Short, 20 mm, and thick. Most stalks obliquely inserted with fleshy bump.
CAVITY	Shallow.
EYE	Medium open. Sepals separated at base, divergent and reflexed, stamens present.
BASIN	Very shallow with slight wrinkles.
SIZE	Medium, 60 mm wide, 90 mm long.
FLESH	Creamy white, sweet, juicy, melting, little flavour but pleasant.
WEIGHT	155 g.
LEAVES	Medium, round oval to oval, medium crenate. Petiole 37 mm.

Plate 6
Fruit A

NAME	***Doyenné Blanc*** Synonyms: many, including *Weisse Herbst Butterbirne, Doyenné, St.Michel, Citron, White Doyenné.*
HISTORY	A very old cultivar of uncertain origin, possibly Italian and first recorded in the seventeenth century. Vigorous and fairly reliably cropping but needs a good summer to develop full flavour.
PICKING TIME	Late September.
SEASON	October.
COLOUR	Pale green changing to pale yellow. Sometimes very faint pinkish orange flush. Little russet, although often small russet patch on one side of the stalk. Lenticels conspicuous as green or russet dots.
SKIN	Smooth
SHAPE	Bergamotte, even.
STALK	Long, 35 mm, woody, curved. Inserted upright or to one side of a fleshy bump. Wrinkles at base of stalk.
CAVITY	Medium.
EYE	Half open, sepals erect, tip reflexed, divided at base. Stamens present.
BASIN	Round and deep.
SIZE	Large, 81 mm wide, 78 mm long.
FLESH	White, melting, fairly juicy, good flavour. Many fruits parthenocarpic with only residual seeds.
WEIGHT	250g.
LEAVES	Medium to large, lanceolate, slightly serrate, almost entire, upfolded. Petiole short 20 mm.

Plate 6
Fruit B

NAME	*Doyenné Bussoch* Synonyms include: *Double Philippe, Doyenné de Merode, Albertine.*
HISTORY	An old Belgian cultivar of uncertain origin. Originally known as *Double Philippe* renamed by Van Mons, *Doyenné de Merode* in honour of Count Merode of Waterloo and subsequently renamed *Doyenné Bussoch* in 1836. Introduced into Britain in 1842. It is reliable and produces a compact spreading tree. It was grown commercially in the 19th century, but the fruit is only second rate and will not store for very long.
PICKING TIME	Mid September.
SEASON	Late September to early October.
COLOUR	Light green turning to bright yellow, occasionally a red flush over quarter to half of the surface. Variable russet, many fruits almost clean with only russet patch near stalk, others up to half covered. Lencicels conspicuous as medium russet dots.
SKIN	Rough.
SHAPE	Variable round with some fruits pyriform. Flattened at base and apex.
STALK	Short and thick, some inserted upright, others obliquely with a bump to one side.
CAVITY	Deep.
EYE	Medium open. Sepals upright, fleshy and fused at base. Stamens sometimes present.
BASIN	Shallow.
SIZE	Medium to large, 70 mm wide, 70 mm long.
FLESH	White, coarse, juicy, no flavour.
WEIGHT	165g or more.
LEAVES	Large, round to oval, coarsely serrate. Petiole 18 mm.

Plate 6
Fruit C

NAME	*Doyenné du Comice*
HISTORY	Raised at the Comice Horticole, Angers, Department of Maine-et Loire, France. First fruited in 1849 and introduced into Britain by Sir Thomas Dyke Acland in 1858. One of the finest pears, it needs a warm sheltered site to grow and crop well. It benefits from training against a warm wall or fence. It is grown commercially throughout the world and on a small scale in Britain. Coloured sports exist including *Red Comice.*
PICKING TIME	Early October.
SEASON	Mid October to mid November.
COLOUR	Pale green changing to pale yellow, some fruits with red flush and sometimes faint stripes. Variable amounts of fine russet, usually patch around eye and stalk. Some fruits completely covered in russet, others clean depending on soil, season and climate. Lenticels fairly inconspicuous as russet or green dots.
SKIN	Some fruits smooth, some slightly rough.
SHAPE	Pyriform, variable, some almost Bergamotte.
STALK	Short to medium, 18 mm, thick, inserted at slight angle with fleshy bump at one side.
CAVITY	None or shallow.
EYE	Medium closed or half open, sepals upright and divided at base.
BASIN	Deep and round with smooth concentric russet.
SIZE	Medium to large, 75 mm wide, 77 mm long (larger fruits more pyriform).
FLESH	Pale yellow, juicy, melting, fine, very slightly gritty at core. Delicious, excellent flavour.
WEIGHT	230 g.
LEAVES	Large, round oval, serrate, upfolded. Petiole 35 mm.

Plate 7
Fruit A

NAME	*Doyenné d'Été* Synonyms include: *Doyenné de Juillet, Jolimont Précoce.*
HISTORY	Raised by the Capucin Monks at Mons probably around 1700. Generally the earliest ripening pear grown and this is its chief virtue. Growth is weak and compact and the most suitable method of growing is a cordon on Quince A rootstock. It is useful as a garden cultivar to extend the pear season. It ripens very soon after picking.
PICKING TIME	Mid July to early August.
SEASON	Mid July to early August.
COLOUR	Bright green changing to pale yellow. Fruits quarter to half flushed with brownish red changing to orange. Some indistinct stripes. Variable amount of russet but fruits mostly clean. Lenticels conspicuous as brown or red dots.
SKIN	Smooth.
SHAPE	Bergamotte to oval. Slightly flattened at apex.
STALK	Medium, 17-25 mm.
CAVITY	Slight.
EYE	Medium closed or half open. Sepals broad based, short , convergent with some tips reflexed appears pinched in. Some stamens present.
BASIN	Very shallow, eye almost on surface.
SIZE	Small, 42 mm side, 45 mm long.
FLESH	White, melting, moderately juicy, sweet with little flavour. Slightly gritty near the core.
WEIGHT	45 g.
LEAVES	Medium, oval, pointed and coarsely serrate. Petiole long, 35 mm.

Plate 7
Fruit B

NAME   *Durondeau*
                Synonym: *De Tongre.*

HISTORY   Raised by M. Durondeau of Tongres-Notre -Dame near
                Tournai, Belgium about 1811. A very attractive fruit of good
                quality, but the trees are not very vigorous and do not grow
                well on light, dry soils.

PICKING TIME   End of September.

SEASON   End of October/November.

COLOUR   Golden yellow, nearly covered by patches and netting of
                golden russet. Most fruits have a red flush. Lenticels are
                conspicuous as large russet dots.

SKIN   Slightly rough, shiny.

SHAPE   Conical, variable, some fruits callabasse. Surface bumpy with
                some fruits hammered.

STALK   Medium length, woody and curved, some stalks have bud and
                leaves. Stalks continued, some with wrinkles at base. Most
                inverted upright, some obliquely with a fleshy bump.

CAVITY   None.

EYE   Half open, sepals medium, appearing pinched in, some tips
                reflexed. Sepals fused at base. Stamens present.

BASIN   Shallow.

SIZE   Medium to large, 65 mm wide, 82 mm long. But some fruits
                larger and callabasse.

FLESH   White, moderately juicy, melting, sweet, pleasant flavour.

WEIGHT   180g.

LEAVES   Medium, oval, shallow crenate, upfolded.

Plate 7
Fruit C

NAME	*Émile d' Heyst* Synonyms: *Heyst Zuckerbirne, Émile, Beurré d'Esperen.*
HISTORY	Raised by Major Esperen at Malines, Belgium and named after M. Émile d' Heyst of Heyst-op-den-Berg. First fruited in 1847. One of the most reliable pears cropping well in most years, even following spring frosts, it can be grown successfully in the North and Scotland.
PICKING TIME	Mid October.
SEASON	November.
COLOUR	Light green turning to yellowish green. Variable amounts of golden brown or brown russet from quarter to almost completely covering fruits. Some solid areas of russet, others mottled. Lenticels conspicuous as large russet dots.
SKIN	Slightly rough.
SHAPE	Oval, symmetrical with one side larger than the other, with a bump to one side of the stalk.
STALK	Medium to long, 22 mm, thick upright or oblique with bump on one side.
CAVITY	Shallow.
EYE	Small to medium, closed or partly open, appearing pinched in. Sepals upright, fleshy, fused at base and pressed together with some tips reflexed. Stamens present.
BASIN	Shallow.
SIZE	Medium, 67 mm wide, 80 mm long.
FLESH	White, slightly yellowish, green beneath skin. Firm, fine, moderately juicy, sweet, subacid pleasant flavour.
WEIGHT	170 g.
LEAVES	Long, pointed, upfolded, medium serrate. Petiole 25 mm.

Plate 7
Fruit D

NAME	*Fertility* Synonym: *Urojainaya* (Russia).
HISTORY	Raised by Rivers of Sawbridgeworth from *Beurré Goubault,* open pollinated. First fruited about 1875. Reliable and heavy cropping but of poor quality. There are many better pears at this season. It was grown commercially in the past. A tetraploid, self fertile sport 'Improved Fertility' exists (discovered at Seabrooks Nurseries), but is not much of an improvement.
PICKING TIME	Mid September.
SEASON	October.
COLOUR	Pale green turning greenish yellow. Variable amounts of russet, some fruits heavily russeted, others with rough russet around stalk and eye and patches on body of fruit. Lenticels fairly inconspicuous as small, black russet dots. Rough.
SHAPE	Conical to pyriform.
STALK	Variable, short to long, 6-25 mm, woody, inserted upright or at a slight angle.
CAVITY	Medium.
EYE	Open, sepals short, erect and divided at base. Stamens present.
BASIN	Eye on level or shallow basin.
SIZE	Small to medium, 66 mm wide, 80 mm long.
FLESH	White, tinged green, juicy, coarse and gritty around the core. Little flavour.
WEIGHT	150g.
LEAVES	Medium, oval, finely serrate. Petiole long, 65 mm.

Plate 8
Fruit A

NAME	*Fondante d'Automne* Synonyms: many, including *Bergamotte Lucrative*.
HISTORY	Raised before 1825 by M. Fiévée at Maubeuge, France. High quality and fairly reliable, good garden cultivar.
PICKING TIME	Mid September.
SEASON	September/October.
COLOUR	Green changing to yellowish green, occasionally very faint pinkish flush over quarter of surface. Netted and mottled brown russet over much of fruit, typically three quarters of surface.
SKIN	Slightly rough to smooth.
SHAPE	Bergamotte, even.
STALK	Short, 10 mm with fleshy bump at either end and so appearing waisted. Inserted centrally or to one side but always upright.
CAVITY	Medium.
EYE	Medium open, sepals upright, claw like and fused at base.
BASIN	Shallow.
SIZE	Medium, 67 mm wide, 69 mm long.
FLESH	White, green tinged beneath skin, fine, melting, juicy. Good flavour.
WEIGHT	200 g.
LEAVES	Round oval, coarsely serrate. Petiole 20 mm.

Plate 8
Fruit B

NAME	*Forelle* Synonyms: *Truitée, Forellenbirne, Trout Pear, Corail.*
HISTORY	The origin of Forelle is uncertain, probably Northern Saxony, Germany and known since 1670. Named because of its prominent lenticel dots resembling the markings of a trout which Forelle is the German word for. It is one of the most attractively coloured pears, but in Britain its flavour rarely matches its appearance and the tree tends to be stunted. It grows and tastes better from warmer climates. It is grown commercially in South Africa and exported to Britain.
PICKING TIME	Mid October.
SEASON	November to January.
COLOUR	Light green turning light yellow, most fruits half to three quarters flushed bright scarlet with some short stripes. Lenticels conspicuous as bright red dots on cheek, red brown or green dots on green areas. Fruits usually russet free.
SKIN	Smooth, shiny.
SHAPE	Very variable, some fruits round or conical, others in particular large ones pyriform.
STALK	Slender, moderate to long, 20 mm, inserted upright or slightly to one side.
CAVITY	Shallow, sometimes with a fleshy wrinkle at the base of stalk.
EYE	Medium open, sepals upright or flattened, fused at their base. Stamens present.
BASIN	Shallow to medium.
SIZE	Small to medium, 55 mm wide, 75 mm long or larger for pyriform fruit. Fruits benefit from thinning.
FLESH	White, melting, juicy, slightly sweet, pleasant, little flavour, slightly gritty at the core.
WEIGHT	120 g or more.
LEAVES	Pointed oval, nearly entire, slightly upfolded. Petiole variable, 35 mm.

Plate 8
Fruit C

NAME	*Glou Morceau*
	Synonyms: *Beurré d'Hardenpont, Hardenponts Winter Butterbirne.*

HISTORY   Raised by one of the pioneers of pear breeding, Abbé Hardenpont of Mons, Belgium about 1750 and introduced into Britain in 1820.
This is an excellent pear which crops reliably and well worth growing benefiting from a warm wall or fence to ripen well. It is sometimes known as *Beurré d'Arenberg* in France, but should not be confused with the *Beurré d'Arenberg* grown in Britain.

PICKING TIME   Mid - late October.

SEASON   December - January.

COLOUR   Pea green turning to pale greenish yellow, very little russet, but a few small russet patches as a result of any slight damage. A little russet spreading from the stalk cavity. Lenticels not very conspicuous as green dots.

SKIN   Smooth.

SHAPE   Oval to pyriform, variable, some fruits tapering towards the eye. Often bossed, bumpy uneven.

STALK   Medium length, 22 mm, thick, upright or at a slight angle.

CAVITY   Fairly deep and narrow.

EYE   Fairly large, open. Sepals upright and wide apart, fused at base and fleshy at base. Stamens present.

BASIN   Wide, deep, uneven and ribbed.

SIZE   Medium to large, 86 mm wide, 100 mm long, but can be smaller if overcropped.

FLESH   White, fine melting, juicy, slightly gritty near the core, good pear flavour, particularly after a hot summer.

WEIGHT   280 g.

LEAVES   Long, oval, finely crenate. Petiole variable, 11 mm or longer.

Plate 8
Fruit D

NAME	*Gorham*
HISTORY	Raised in 1910 by Richard Wellington at New York State Agricultural Experimental Station from *Williams Bon Chrétien* x *Josephine de Malines*. Introduced in 1923. A good quality and reliable pear but sometimes only of moderate cropping. A good garden cultivar following on in season from *Williams Bon Chrétien*.
PICKING TIME	Early to mid September.
SEASON	Mid September to early October.
COLOUR	Pale green changing to pale yellow. Light brown russet patches spreading from stalk and patches and streaks across the fruit. Some fruits heavily russetted, others quite clean. Commonly about half covered in russet. Lenticels fairly inconspicuous as small russet dots.
SKIN	Fairly smooth.
SHAPE	Very variable, conical, pyriform to oval.
STALK	Medium length, 20 mm, thick, usually obliquely inserted with fleshy bump behind.
CAVITY	Fairly deep.
EYE	Medium open, sepals erect and fused at base. Stamens present.
BASIN	Medium width and medium depth.
SIZE	Small to medium, 63 mm wide, 91 mm long.
FLESH	Cream, fine, juicy, sweet musky flavour.
WEIGHT	210 g.
LEAVES	Oval, upcupped, serrate. Petiole 22 mm.

Plate 9
Fruit A

NAME	*Hessle* Synonyms: a number of variations in spelling including *Hessel* and *Hazel.*
HISTORY	Origin uncertain, probably arose at Hessle near Hull, East Yorkshire. First recorded in 1827, but probably much older. A very hardy pear widely grown in the North of England and Scotland in the past and many old trees still in existence. Reliable and worth growing as a garden cultivar in cooler areas but there are much better pears at this season for growing in more favourable areas.
PICKING TIME	Early September.
SEASON	September/October.
COLOUR	Greenish yellow, some fruits heavily russeted and others fairly clean particularly in the south of England. Many with russet patch around the stem. Lenticels conspicuous as large russet dots.
SKIN	Smooth, some fruits slightly rough.
SHAPE	Round conical.
STALK	Medium length, 18 mm, fairly thick, some inserted upright others obliquely inserted.
CAVITY	Small, shallow with some russet.
EYE	Medium open, sepals large, upright and russet at base.
BASIN	Shallow.
SIZE	Small, 48 mm wide, 50 mm long.
FLESH	White, juicy, fairly sweet, gritty around the core, little flavour.
WEIGHT	55 g.
LEAVES	Long, oval, entire. Petiole long 44 mm.

Plate 9
Fruit B

NAME	*Jargonelle* Synonyms: many including *English Jargonelle* and variations of spelling also *Grosse Cuisse Madame,* etc.
HISTORY	Origin uncertain, one of the most ancient pears in cultivation, first mentioned by Parkinson in 1629 but possibly much older. One of the hardiest and longest lived pears which was grown throughout Britain including Scotland. It is still worth growing in colder areas and also has some resistance to scab. It is partially tip bearing and so best grown as a bush tree. Timing of picking is important as it has a tendency to rot from the core.
PICKING TIME	Early to mid August.
SEASON	Mid - late August.
COLOUR	Mid green ripening to greenish yellow with a brownish red flush on some fruits. Some russet patches, a patch spreading from the stalk and other variable patches over up quarter of the fruit. Lenticels inconspicuous as green or occasionally brown dots.
SKIN	Smooth or slightly rough where russetted.
SHAPE	Long conical to pyriform.
STALK	Long, 35-45 mm, obliquely inserted and characteristically curved with fleshy bump.
CAVITY	Stem continued or slight depression on one side.
EYE	Large, open, sepals long and fleshy, often with fleshy bumps at base but separated at base, tips reflexed. Stamens present.
BASIN	Very shallow, eye almost on surface.
SIZE	Medium, 55 wide, 90 mm long.
FLESH	Pale yellow, tender and juicy with slight musky flavour, gritty near the core.
WEIGHT	150 g.
LEAVES	Large, oval, pointed, coarsely serrate, upfolded. Petiole long 45 mm.

Plate 9
Fruit C

NAME	*Josephine de Malines*
HISTORY	Raised in about 1830 by Major Esperen at Malines, Belgium and named after his wife. A very good winter pear. Tree growth is weak to moderate and so Quince A is generally the best rootstock. It is best grown against a south, south-west or west facing wall or fence to ripen well. It shows good resistance to pear scab.
PICKING TIME	Late October.
SEASON	January to February.
COLOUR	Pale green turning to yellowish green. Variable amount of greenish russet. Some fruits with just a patch around stem. Others with mottled russet over much of surface. Lenticels fairly inconspicuous as small russet dots.
SKIN	Smooth or slightly rough if heavily russetted.
SHAPE	Bergamotte to short conical.
STALK	Short, 20 mm, thick, inserted at a slight angle.
CAVITY	Shallow.
EYE	Small, open, sepals short and fused at base. Stamens present.
BASIN	Shallow.
SIZE	Small, 62 mm wide, 60 mm long.
FLESH	White, tinged green under skin. Fine, melting, sweet and moderately juicy.
WEIGHT	130 g.
LEAVES	Very small, oval to lanceolate, crenate. Petiole long, 25 mm.

Plate 9
Fruit D

NAME	*Jules d'Airolles*
HISTORY	This was probably obtained by M. Leon Leclerc of Laval Mayence, France in 1836 (there have been 2 pears with this name in the past). A highly coloured good quality pear which crops reliably at Wisley.
PICKING TIME	Early to mid October.
SEASON	November.
COLOUR	Pale green turning to pale yellow; most fruits flushed with bright red over half to three quarters of the fruit, also some indistinct stripes. Some small russet patches and a russet patch around the stalk but not the eye. Lenticels fairly inconspicuous as russet or green dots.
SKIN	Smooth.
SHAPE	Pyriform, tapering to the eye.
STALK	Short to medium, variable, 20 mm, medium thickness and woody. Inserted upright between two fleshy bumps or at an angle beside one fleshy bump.
CAVITY	Medium, narrow.
EYE	Half open, sepals short, erect and fused at base.
BASIN	Medium width and shallow to medium depth.
SIZE	Medium to large, 70 mm wide, 110 mm long.
FLESH	Yellowish, juicy, sweet, delicious and aromatic, slightly astringent flavour. Slightly gritty at the core.
WEIGHT	250 g.
LEAVES	Oval, medium serrate, slightly downfolded. Petiole 30 mm.

Plate 10
Fruit A

NAME	*Laxton's Foremost*
HISTORY	Raised in 1901 by Laxton Bros of Bedford from *Marechal de Cour* x *Fertility* and introduced in 1939. One of a number of pears raised by Laxton Bros. Reliable cropping with a compact upright habit. It is now little grown.
PICKING TIME	Early to mid September.
SEASON	Mid to late September.
COLOUR	Pale green turning yellow. Faint pinkish red flush and faint stripes. A variable amount of russet. A patch around and spreading from the stalk, some other patches. Some fruits very russetted, others almost clean. Lenticels small but conspicuous as brown russet dots.
SKIN	Smooth.
SHAPE	Conical to long conical, variable.
STALK	Short, 10 mm and thick, some inserted upright with a bump on each side. Others inserted obliquely with a fleshy bump.
CAVITY	Very shallow.
EYE	Small, open. Sepals small to medium, divergent and fused at base.
BASIN	Shallow.
SIZE	Medium, 60 mm wide, 80 mm long.
FLESH	Creamy, yellowish white, coarse, juicy and pleasant but little flavour.
WEIGHT	180 g.
LEAVES	Oval, pointed, medium crenate, upfolded. Petiole 35 mm long.

Plate 10
Fruit B

NAME	*Le Brun*
HISTORY	Raised about 1856 by M. Gueniot at Troyes, France and first fruited in 1862. It crops reliably with heavy crops of large fruits but not of great quality.
PICKING TIME	Mid September.
SEASON	October.
COLOUR	Light green turning light greenish yellow, some patches of brown russet with small patches around stalk, but fruit mostly clean. Some fruits with slight red flush. Lenticels small and fairly conspicuous as green, brown russet dots or red on flush.
SKIN	Smooth.
SHAPE	Long callabasse, slightly bumpy.
STALK	Short and very thick, 20 mm long. Some inserted upright or at slight angle, others almost at a right angle with fleshy bump on one side. When inserted upright there is a bump on each side.
CAVITY	When stalk is upright, a fairly deep cavity.
EYE	Half open and appears pinched in. Sepals fairly short, fused at base and erect.
BASIN	Moderately deep and wide and even. Some with wavy hair lines present.
SIZE	Large, 70 mm wide, 120 mm long.
FLESH	Yellowish white, fine grained, slightly gritty near the core, sweet, melting with scented light flavour. Fruit examined were parthenocarpic with no seeds present.
WEIGHT	300 g.
LEAVES	Oval, pointed, finely serrate.

Plate 10
Fruit C

NAME	*Louise Bonne of Jersey* Synonyms: including *Louise Bonne d'Avranches*.
HISTORY	Raised about 1780 by M. Longueval, Avranches, Normandy, France. The English name arose as an error presumably because it arrived via the Channel Islands. It is an attractive, reliable and good quality pear, heavy cropping (often requiring thinning) and a good garden cultivar. It is moderately vigorous, growing well in all forms.
PICKING TIME	Mid - late September.
SEASON	October.
COLOUR	Pale green turning pale yellowish green. Red flush with prominent red haloes to lenticels. Lenticels elsewhere conspicuous as green or russet dots. A little russet around stalk but generally clean.
SKIN	Smooth.
SHAPE	Conical, even.
STALK	Short to long variable, medium thickness and woody, inserted upright or at a slight angle.
CAVITY	Variable from none to medium depth.
EYE	Medium, open, sepals fused at base. Stamens present.
BASIN	Medium, even.
SIZE	Small to medium, 65 mm wide, 100 mm long.
FLESH	White, sweet, juicy, melting with good pleasant flavour. Some fruits parthenocarpic.
WEIGHT	130 g but sometimes more.
LEAVES	Oval, finely serrate. Petiole 37 mm.

Plate 10
Fruit D

NAME	*Marguerite Marillat*
HISTORY	Raised in 1872 by M. Marillat of Craponne near Lyons, France. An attractive and distinctive fruit of reasonable quality. The tree is of erect habit with compact spurs and crops reliably. It was quite widely grown for market in Britain earlier this century and can still be found in old orchards and gardens.
PICKING TIME	Early to mid September.
SEASON	Mid September to early October.
COLOUR	Pale green turning to pale golden yellow. Bright pink red flush and stripes over quarter to half of surface of the fruit. Some russet spreading from stem and eye. Sometimes further small or large russet patches but generally clean. Lenticels conspicuous as brown russet dots.
SKIN	Smooth or slightly rough if russetted.
SHAPE	Conical to callabasse, uneven, bumpy and asymmetric.
STALK	Short, 5-15 mm , very thick inserted at 90 or less to axis of pear with fleshy bump above it.
CAVITY	None, continued but depression where stalk turned over.
EYE	Medium open, sepals fused at base and erect with tips reflexed and downy.
BASIN	Moderately wide and deep.
SIZE	Large, 69 mm wide, 100 mm long.
FLESH	Creamy pale yellow, juicy, slightly gritty near core with pleasant mild flavour.
WEIGHT	225 g.
LEAVES	Medium, round oval, pointed, shallow serrate. Petiole fairly short 13-20 mm.

Plate 11
Fruit A

NAME	*Marie Louise* Synonyms: many including *Marie Louise Delcourt, Princess de Parme.*
HISTORY	Raised by the Abbé Duquesne of Mons, Belgium in 1809 and named after Napoleon's second wife, the Archduchess of Austria. Considered a good pear in the past and widely planted in gardens but not very reliable and now little grown.
PICKING TIME	Late September.
SEASON	October.
COLOUR	Pale green turning to pale greenish yellow with some brown russet patches, but mostly clean.
SKIN	Smooth.
SHAPE	Oval.
STALK	Long, woody, curved, 33 mm long, upright but inserted to one side or at an angle.
CAVITY	Very shallow.
EYE	Open, sepals fused at base, divergent and often erect. Stamens present.
BASIN	Very shallow, eye almost on the surface.
SIZE	Medium, 62 mm wide, 94 mm long.
FLESH	White, very juicy, gritty particularly around the core, light flavour.
WEIGHT	180 g.
LEAVES	Narrow oval, coarse but shallow serrate. Petiole 22 mm.

Plate 11
Fruit B

NAME	*Marie Louise d'Uccle*
HISTORY	Raised by M. Gambier of Rhode, St. Genese near Brussel from *Marie Louise* open pollinated and first fruited in 1846. A reliably cropping and good quality pear which deserves to be more widely cultivated although it is apparently rather susceptible to scab.
PICKING TIME	Mid to late September.
SEASON	October.
COLOUR	Yellowish green turning to golden yellow. A lot of golden brown russet patches and dots distributed over about half of the fruit surface. Red flush on some fruits over third of surface. Lenticels fairly inconspicuous as small russet or red dots.
SKIN	Rough.
SHAPE	Conical to pyriform variable.
STALK	Medium length, woody, generally at an angle with a fleshy bump to one side. Some stalks have buds and leaves.
CAVITY	Shallow.
EYE	Open, star like, sepals quite long and fused at base. Stamens present.
BASIN	Medium width and depth.
SIZE	Medium to large, 75 mm wide, 81 mm long.
FLESH	Pale yellow, fine, melting, juicy with very good flavour.
WEIGHT	220 g.
LEAVES	Fairly large, oval, medium serrate. Petiole long 50 mm.

Plate 11
Fruit C

NAME	*Merton Pride* Synonyms: J.I. 4016, *Merton Favourite*.
HISTORY	Raised in 1941 by M.B. Crane at the John Innes Horticultural Institute, Merton from *Glou Morceau* x *Double Williams*. Named *Merton Favourite* in 1953 and renamed *Merton Pride* in 1957. Introduced in 1959. An excellent pear for garden cultivation, one of the juiciest pears grown and one of the best of its season. It is triploid and vigorous so it is usually best to grow it on Quince C rootstock.
PICKING TIME	Early September.
SEASON	Mid to late September.
COLOUR	Green turning yellow. A lot of russet around the stalk and eye and netted elsewhere. Fruits never in my experience clean of russet and sometimes totally russetted. Lenticels inconspicuous.
SKIN	Slightly rough to rough.
SHAPE	Pyriform to conical.
STALK	Short to medium, 20 mm long and medium width. Inserted centrally with a slight bump on each side or sometimes at a slight angle with a slight bump on one side.
CAVITY	Medium.
EYE	Open, sepals broad based, fused, divergent with tips reflexed. Stamens present.
BASIN	Medium.
SIZE	Large, 72 mm wide, 90 mm long.
FLESH	Creamy white, soft, melting, fine, very juicy, sweet with excellent pear flavour.
WEIGHT	210 g.
LEAVES	Large oval, crenate. Petiole 37 mm long.

Plate 11
Fruit D

NAME	*Michaelmas Nelis* Synonym: *Michaelmas*
HISTORY	Raised in a cottage garden near Gravesend in Kent from *Winter Nelis* open pollinated. Introduced by Messrs Bunyard & Co in 1900. A good quality autumn pear but cropping only light to moderate.
PICKING TIME	Early September.
SEASON	Mid to late September.
COLOUR	Yellowish green turning to pale yellow. Variable russet, some fruits almost clean except russet around eye. Some fruits almost entirely russetted. Generally no russet around stalk. Lenticels conspicuous as russet or green dots.
SKIN	Smooth or slightly rough if russetted.
SHAPE	Round to round conical.
STALK	Long, 30 mm long and medium thickness.
CAVITY	Deep and narrow.
EYE	Open, sepals erect, fused at base and downy.
BASIN	Shallow and medium width.
SIZE	Medium, 62 mm wide, 62 mm long.
FLESH	Pale yellow, melting, sweet with good aromatic pear flavour.
WEIGHT	130 g.
LEAVES	Long oval, coarsely serrate. Petiole short 18 mm.

Plate 12
Fruit A

NAME	*Nouveau Poiteau*
HISTORY	Raised by Van Mons at Louvain, Belgium in 1827, first fruited in 1843. It was named after the pomologist Poiteau. Reliable and heavy cropping of medium vigour, a good garden cultivar.
PICKING TIME	Early to mid October.
SEASON	November.
COLOUR	Green turning pale green. Some fruits with a slight red flush. Variable russet, some fruits fairly clean others heavily russeted. Russet patch around stalk and other patches. Lenticels conspicuous as russet dots.
SKIN	Rough.
SHAPE	Oval pyriform.
STALK	Short ot medium, thick, upright or at slight angle, continued.
CAVITY	None or slight cavity.
EYE	Closed or slightly open, sepals short, fused at base and divergent. Stamens present.
BASIN	Shallow.
SIZE	Medium, 57 mm wide, 80 mm long or larger.
FLESH	White, green under skin. Sweet, juicy, melting, good flavour.
WEIGHT	150 g or more.
LEAVES	Oval, upfolded, fine crenate. Petiole 30 mm.

Plate 12
Fruit B

NAME	*Olivier de Serres*

HISTORY Raised in the mid 19th century by M. Boisbunel of Rouen from *Forunée d'Angers* open pollinated and first fruited in 1861, named after Olivier de Serres a famous agronomist of the late 16th and early 17th centuries. It is a very fine winter pear but its growth is weak and compact and it is best suited to growing against a warm south, southwest or west facing wall or fence. A good garden cultivar for favourable locations.

PICKING TIME Late October to early November.

SEASON February to April.

COLOUR Light green showing little colour change. Most fruits heavily russetted with brown russet over three quarters to most of fruit. Lenticels conspicuous as medium russet dots.

SKIN Rough.

SHAPE Round or flat round, apple shaped.

STALK Short, 15 mm and fairly thick.

CAVITY Deep and narrow.

EYE Small. Sepals and stamens absent.

BASIN Deep and narrow.

SIZE Small, 54 mm wide, 48 mm long.

FLESH White, green under the skin. Sweet with balancing acidity, rich aromatic flavour, moderately juicy.

WEIGHT 90 g.

LEAVES Small, narrow, oval to lanceolate, serrate. Petiole long, 35 mm.

Plate 12
Fruit C

NAME	*Onward*
HISTORY	Raised in 1947 at National Fruit Trials Wisley, Surrey from *Laxton's Superb* x *Doyenné du Comice* and named in 1967. An excellent quality pear, one of the best of its season. It crops reliably even in years with spring frosts. One of the best pears for garden cultivation but will not pollinate *Doyenné du Comice* and vice versa.
PICKING TIME	Early September. It does not drop from the tree and so must be checked carefully for ripeness.
SEASON	Mid September to early October.
COLOUR	Light green changing to yellow green, many fruits with pinkish red flush and stripes over up to half of surface. Light brown russet at stalk and eye and dots, patches and streaks elsewhere. Some fruits heavily russetted. Lenticels conspicuous as green or brown russet dots.
SKIN	Smooth.
SHAPE	Pyriform, variable, some fruits bergamotte or conical. Slightly bumpy particularly towards stalk.
STALK	Variable, short to long, 20-55 mm and thick. Some stalks with buds. Inserted upright on level with wrinkle at base.
CAVITY	None, inserted on level with fleshy wrinkle.
EYE	Medium, closed. Sepals medium, fleshy, separated at base and clasped together.
BASIN	Medium width and depth.
SIZE	Medium, 63 mm wide, 85 mm long.
FLESH	Creamy white, melting, very fine, juicy, sweet rich flavour with balancing acidity, excellent.
WEIGHT	170 g.
LEAVES	Medium, oval, medium serrate. Petiole 18 mm.

Plate 12
Fruit D

NAME	*Packham's Triumph*

HISTORY Raised about 1896 by Charles Henry Packham at Molong, New South Wales, Australia from *Uvedale's St Germain* x *Williams Bon Chrétien* and inroduced early this century, but not widely available until the 1940's.
A good quality and reliable pear grown commercially extensively in Australia and elsewhere and to a small extent in Britain.

PICKING TIME Late September to early October.

SEASON October - November.

COLOUR Bright green changing to pale yellow. Little russet except a small patch at stalk and eye. Lenticels conspicuous as small russet dots.

SKIN Smooth but surface of fruit bumpy.

SHAPE Pyriform, bumpy, stalk obliquely inserted with fleshy bump.

STALK Medium, 25 mm long, woody, curved often obliquely inserted but sometimes upright or at right angle.

CAVITY None or very shallow.

EYE Open. Sepals fused at base and flattened, star like. Stamens present.

BASIN Very shallow.

SIZE Medium to large but can be small if not thinned, 67 mm wide, 80 mm long.

FLESH Pale yellow, juicy, fine with a musky flavour.

WEIGHT 170 g.

LEAVES Small, oval, upcupped, crenate. Petiole 30 mm.

Plate 13
Fruit A

NAME	*Passe Crassanne*
HISTORY	Raised by M. Boisbunel of Ruen, France in 1845 and first fruited in 1855. This is a good quality late pear but does not generally ripen well in Britain requiring a warm wall or fence. Imported fruits form Italy are of better flavour.
PICKING TIME	Late October.
SEASON	February to March.
COLOUR	Dull green turning to dull yellow, variable amount of russet from one quarter to almost completely russetted with brown rough russet, patches spreading from stalk and eye. Lenticels fairly conspicuous as medium russet dots. Imported fruit is generally less russeted.
SKIN	Rough.
SHAPE	Round, oval, uneven and bossed on surface.
STALK	Medium length 20 mm, thick and woody, inserted upright.
CAVITY	Narrow and deep.
EYE	Open, sepals long, upright and fused at base. Stamens present.
BASIN	Fairly wide and deep and uneven.
SIZE	Large, 74 mm wide, 69 mm long.
FLESH	Creamy white, slightly gritty at the core, fine and juicy, reasonable flavour. Good after a hot summer or in a warmer climate.
WEIGHT	220 g.
LEAVES	Oval, tapering equally at each end, upfolded, undulating, shallow serrate or almost entire. Petiole 25 mm long.

Plate 13
Fruit B

NAME	*Pitmaston Duchess*
	Synonyms: including *Pitmaston Duchesse d'Angouleme, Williams Duchesse.*

HISTORY

Raised in 1841 by John Williams at Pitmaston, Worcestershire from *Duchesse d'Angouleme* x *Glou Morceau*. Original name *Pitmaston Duchesse d'Angouleme*, renamed 1870.
A vigorous triploid cultivar of good quality but subject to scab.
A good garden cultivar where space allows cultivation as a bush tree, rather too vigorous for growing in restricted form.

PICKING TIME

Mid - late September.

SEASON

October.

COLOUR

Light green changing to pale yellow sometimes slight red flush. Brown russet around stalk and spreading a little, other variable patches on body. Lenticels fairly inconspicuous as brown or russet dots.

SKIN

Smooth, except where there is russet.

SHAPE

Long conical to pyriform.

STALK

Short to long, variable, thick inserted at slight angle to one side.

CAVITY

Medium.

EYE

Medium, closed, sepals upright with tips reflexed and fused at base.

BASIN

Fairly deep and medium width.

SIZE

Very large, 93 mm wide, 127 mm long.
Some fruits parthenocarpic (lacking seeds).

FLESH

Yellowish white, melting, juicy, slightly gritty around the core. Good flavour.

WEIGHT

500 g.

LEAVES

Very large, round oval, variable, coarse and irregularly serrate. Petiole long, 45 mm. Dark red autumn colour.

Plate 13
Fruit C

NAME	*Précoce de Trévoux*
HISTORY	First described in 1862. It was obtained by M. Treyve of Trévoux, Ain, France. One of the finest flavoured and highest quality early pears but it flowers early and so does not always crop reliably. Best grown in an area free from spring frosts and sheltered from strong winds. Tree growth is moderate.
PICKING TIME	Mid- late August.
SEASON	Early September.
COLOUR	Pale green changing to yellow. Most fruits half to three quarters flushed with bright carmine red right around to the eye of the fruit with the sepals bases also red. Some russet streaks from the stalk and across the surface of some fruits. Lenticels conspicuous as medium russet dots.
SKIN	Smooth or slightly rough where russet present.
SHAPE	Pyriform, flattened at base (eye end).
STALK	Short, 15 mm long thick with fleshy bump at base. Inserted at a slight angle.
CAVITY	Fairly deep.
EYE	Medium tightly closed, sepals broad based, fleshy and fused at base, pinched in with tips reflexed.
BASIN	Medium to deep and round.
SIZE	Medium to large, 76 mm wide, 100 mm long.
FLESH	White, juicy, buttery, excellent, rich flavour with some perfume and musk flavour.
WEIGHT	240 g.
LEAVES	Medium, oval, medium serrate. Periole variable, 30 mm.

Plate 14
Fruit A

NAME	*Princess*
HISTORY	Raised by Rivers of Sawbridgeworth about 1875 from *Louise Bonne of Jersey* open pollinated. An attractive pear, very similar to *Louise Bonne of Jersey* but much larger and of poorer flavour.
PICKING TIME	Late September.
SEASON	Mid to late October.
COLOUR	Pale green turning pale yellow. Variable pinkish red flush covering up to about half of surface. Variable russet with small patches at eye and stalk but most fruits almost clean. Lenticels fairly conspicuous as green dots.
SKIN	Smooth.
SHAPE	Long conical even. Surface slightly bumpy.
STALK	Short, 12 mm, medium thickness, obliquely inserted with bump behind it.
CAVITY	Shallow.
EYE	Half open, sepals medium, upright, separated at base with stamens present.
BASIN	Medium width and medium depth.
SIZE	Medium to large, 70 mm wide, 115 mm long.
FLESH	White, fine, buttery, juicy, sweet and pleasant but little flavour.
WEIGHT	240 g.
LEAVES	Small, oval, pointed, coarsely crenate. Petiole 25 mm.

Plate 14
Fruit B

NAME	*Souvenir du Congrès*
HISTORY	Raised in 1852 by M. Morel at Lyon-Vaise, France and first fruited in 1863. A similar pear to *Williams Bon Chrétien*. It makes a compact tree and crops heavily. It is generally not as good as *Williams Bon Chrétien* except that it reputedly has better resistance to scab.
PICKING TIME	Early to mid September.
SEASON	Mid to late September.
COLOUR	Pale green turning to light yellow, many fruits with scarlet flush and indistinct stripes over quarter to half of surface. A variable amount of light brown russet. Russet patches at stalk and eye and some other patches and dots but mainly russet free. Lenticels conspicuous as green or brown russet dots.
SKIN	Smooth.
SHAPE	Callabasse with some fruits conical, flattened at eye (it stands up easily), bumpy and uneven.
STALK	Short to medium, 20 mm long, thick, inserted obliquely with a bump to one side. Some fruits have stalks inserted upright.
CAVITY	Medium.
EYE	Small open, sepals small and flattened.
BASIN	Deep.
SIZE	Large, 85 mm wide, 98 mm long (but can be smaller if not thinned).
FLESH	Pale yellow, tender, sweet and juicy with musky flavour.
WEIGHT	240 g.
LEAVES	Large, round to roundish oval, variable, medium crenate. Petiole long 50 mm.

74

Plate 14
Fruit C

NAME	*Thompsons*
	Synonyms: *Van Mons, Vlesembeek.*

HISTORY   Believed to be a seedling raised by Van Mons in Belgium sent to England about 1820 without a name. Named after Robert Thompson, then Fruit Foreman at the RHS Garden Chiswick by Joseph Sabine, Secretary of the RHS (1816-1830).
A good quality pear, growth and cropping moderate.

PICKING TIME   End of September.

SEASON   October/November.

COLOUR   Pale green turning to pale golden yellow. Variable amount of brown russet over up to half of the fruit. Lenticels not very conspicuous as greenish russet dots. Always a russet patch around the stalk.

SKIN   Rough.

SHAPE   Oval to pyriform, uneven, bumpy.

STALK   Short, 12 mm long and woody, generally inserted at an angle with a small bump to one side.

CAVITY   Narrow, medium depth.

EYE   Small, half open. Sepals erect and fused at base.

BASIN   Narrow and medium depth.

SIZE   Medium to large, 70 mm wide, 83 mm long.

FLESH   Creamy white, smooth, melting, juicy. Delicious aromatic flavour.

WEIGHT   220 g.

LEAVES   Oval undulating, sharply serrate. They show good autumn colour.

Plate 14
Fruit D

NAME	*Uvedale's St Germain* Synonyms: many including *Belle Angevine* and *Pound*.
HISTORY	Origin uncertain, reputedly raised about 1690 by Dr Uvedale, a schoolmaster, amateur botanist and collector of Eltham in Kent and Enfield (Dr Uvedale's herbarium is held by the Natural History Museum). It was incorrectly named *Belle Angevine* in France and Pound in US. It is one of the Warden group of cooking pears and needs to be cooked slowly for 1-2 hours. Tree growth is vigorous and it is heavy cropping. It is triploid. It is not as good as some of the other cooking pears such as *Catillac, Bellisime D'Hiver* and *Black Worcester* and so not worth planting although many old trees still exist.
PICKING TIME	Late October.
SEASON	January - March.
COLOUR	Light green changing to pale yellow. Some fruits with faint orange red flush and indistinct stripes (fruits from France are much highly coloured). Variable brown russet patches usually with a patch around the stalk (but mostly clean). Lenticels conspicuous as medium to large russet dots.
SKIN	Smooth.
SHAPE	Pyriform to long pyriform or calabasse, uneven , tapering towards eye.
STALK	Medium length, 30 mm, thick and curved, inserted upright with three fleshy bumps at its base or at a slight angle with one bump often with fleshy wrinkle.
CAVITY	Shallow with fleshy wrinkle and surrounded by bumps.
EYE	Closed. Sepals fused at base, upright, pressed together with tips reflexed.
BASIN	Very shallow.
SIZE	Large to very large, 79 mm wide, 110 mm long or much larger.

FLESH   White, tinged green under skin, gritty particularly near the core, crisp, no flavour raw.

WEIGHT   310 g but can be 500 g or more.

LEAVES   Oval, pointed. Coarsely serrate. Petiole short 19 mm.

Plate 15
Fruit A

NAME	*Vicar of Winkfield* Synonyms: *Curé, Pastorenbirn.*
HISTORY	Discovered about 1760 by M. Leroy, Curé at Villers-en-Brenne, France growing in a wood nearby. It was introduced into Britain by the Rev. W.L. Rham of Winkfield, Berkshire hence its name. This is a culinary pear of reasonable flavour when cooked but scarcely worth growing, it has a habit of dropping a lot of fruit before it is ready to pick. This early fruit then shrivels in storage.
PICKING TIME	Early to late September.
SEASON	November to January.
COLOUR	Green changing to pale yellowish green with slight brownish flush on some fruits. Lenticels conspicuous as green or russet dots. Variable amount of russet patches and sometimes lines, but some fruits quite clean.
SKIN	Smooth.
SHAPE	Long callabasse, some fruits uneven.
STALK	Medium to long, 28 mm, woody, inserted at a slight angle often with a fleshy bump on one side.
CAVITY	None.
EYE	Wide, open, sepals wide and flattened outwards, star like and fused at base. Stamens sometimes present.
BASIN	Medium width and shallow.
SIZE	Large, 66 mm wide, 116 mm long.
FLESH	Pale yellow, dry and soft, little favour raw. When cooked light flavour, fine flesh but fibrous near core.
WEIGHT	210 g.
LEAVES	Round, pointed, upcupped, irregularly serrate. Petiole 27 mm.

Plate 15
Fruit B

NAME	*Williams' Bon Chrétien* Synonyms: many including *Aldermaston Pear, Bartlett, Stairs Pear.*
HISTORY	Originated as a seedling or possibly raised prior to 1770 in the garden of a schoolmaster, Mr Wheeler at Aldermaston, Berkshire. The next schoolmaster to have the garden, Mr Stair sent grafts to a nurseryman Richard Williams of Turnham Green. The pear was named after him by Mr Aiton in 1814. It was imported at the end of the 18th century to USA by James Carter for Thomas Brewer of Roxbury, Massachussetts. His land was later acquired by Enoch Bartlett who not knowing its name gave it his name in 1817. Hence both in Britain and the USA it acquired the name of the distributer not the raiser. The most widely grown pear in the world although now little grown commercially in Britain, it provided the foundation for the American canned pear trade. There are several red sports in existence including *Glow Red Williams*. It has been extensively used in breeding programmes. It is a good quality early pear, cropping heavily and reliably and moderately vigorous. Correct timing of picking is critical, too late and it will tend to rot from the core. Although in most ways a good garden pear it has the serious drawback of being rather susceptible to scab and so not suited to wetter parts of the country and it may be necessary to spray to control scab.
PICKING TIME	Early September.
SEASON	Mid - late September.
COLOUR	Pale green turning to golden yellow, some fruits with very faint red stripes. Variable russet with patch around the stalk and marbling on the fruit. Some fruits are almost clean. Lenticels conspicuous as small russet dots.
SKIN	Smooth.
SHAPE	Pyriform uneven. Some fruits with stalk inserted centrally and some inserted obliquely.
STALK	Short, 15 mm and thick.
CAVITY	Medium.

EYE	Medium, open. Sepals short, upright, divided at base.
BASIN	Shallow, pinched in, hence oval rather than round.
SIZE	Medium to large, 70 mm wide, 82 mm long.
FLESH	White, very juicy, sweet with a strong musky flavour.
WEIGHT	210 g.
LEAVES	Round to round oval, fine to medium serrate. Petiole fairly short, 21 mm.

Plate 15
Fruit C

NAME	*Winter Nelis*
	Synonyms: *Nelis d'Hiver, Coloma d'Hiver, Bonne de Malines.*

HISTORY Raised by Jean Charles Nelis at Malines early in the 19th century and introduced to Britain in 1818.
A good late pear, cropping reliably but tree growth is weak and trees should be grown on Quince A (Quince C is too dwarfing). Fruits tend to be small and often require thinning.

PICKING TIME Late October.

SEASON December to January.

COLOUR Pale green turning to pale yellowish green, fruits three quarters or more covered by russet much of it continuous, also spots and patches. More russet at eye than at stalk. Lenticels not very conspicuous as small russet dots.

SKIN Rough.

SHAPE Round conical.

STALK Long, variable, 20 to 30 mm in length, medium thickness, woody. Inserted upright but curved.

CAVITY Medium depth and narrow.

EYE Medium size, open, sepals upright, fused at base, tips bent in. Stamens present.

BASIN Small, round, even, medium to deep.

SIZE Small to medium, 60 mm wide, 60 mm long.

FLESH Greenish white, juicy, sweet, good flavour.

WEIGHT 110 g.

LEAVES Characteristically small, narrow lanceolate, very shallow serrate, most entire. Petiole long 44 mm.

Bibliography

1. Baker, Harry. *The Fruit Garden Displayed.* Eight Edition. Cassel Educational Ltd. London, 1991.

2. Brooks, Reid M., Olmo H.P. *Register of New Fruit and Nut Varieties.* Second Edition. University of California Press Ltd. Berkeley, Los Angeles, London, 1972.

3. Bunyard, Edward A. *A Handbook of Hardy Fruits. Apples and Pears.* John Murray. London,1920.

4. Garner, R.J. *The Grafter's Handbook.* Faber and Faber. London & Boston, 1979.

5. Hedrick, U.P. *The Pears of New York.* Albany. New York, 1921.

6. Hogg, Robert. *The Fruit Manual.* Fifth Edition. Journal of Horticulture Office. London,1884.

7. Luckwill, L.C. & Pollard, A. *Perry Pears.* University of Bristol,1963.

8. Petzold, Herbert. *Birnensorten.* Verlag J. Neumann-Neudamm. Melsungen, 1984.

9. Roach, F.A. *Cultivated Fruits of Britain. Their Origin and History.* Basil Blackwell Ltd. Oxford, 1985.

10. Scott, John. *The Orchardist.* London, 1869.

11. Smith, Muriel W.G. *Catalogue of British Pears.* M.A.F.F., A.D.A.S., 1976.

12. White, Allan G. *Nashi. Asian Pear in New Zealand.* DSIR. Wellington, 1990.

APPENDIX I

Pears recognised as Perry Pears by the Ministry of Agriculture Fisheries and Food in 1989

The following varieties of pears are perry pears

Variety	*Synonym(s)*
Arlingham Squash	Squash Pear, Old Squash, Old Taynton Squash
Barland	
Barnet	Barn Pear, Brown Thorn Pear, Hedgehog Pear
Bartestree Squash	
Bastard Longdon	
Bastard Sack	
Billy Williams	
Black Huffcap	Black Pear
Blacksmith	
Blakeney Red	Blakeney, Red Pear, Circus Pear, Painted Lady, Painted Pear
Bloody Bastard	
Bosbury Scarlet	
Boy Pear	
Brandy	
Brockhill	
Brown Bess	Brown Bessie
Brown Russet	
Butt	Norton Butt
Cannock	
Chaceley Green	Chaseley Green
Claret	
Clipper Dick	
Clusters	
Coppy	Coppice
Cowslip	
Deadboy	
Ducksbarn	Duckbarn, Ducksbourne
Early Blet	
Early Griffin	Griffin's Early
Early Hay Pear	Hay Pear
Early Longdon	
Early Treacle	
Flakey Bark	
Forrest Pear	
Gin	
Golden Balls	
Goldings	
Grandfather Tum(p)	

The following varieties of pears are perry pears

Variety	Synonym(s)
Green Horse	Horse Pear
Green Longdon	Brown Longdon, Longdon, Longland(s), Old Fashioned Longdon, Russet Longdon
Gregg's Pit	
Hampton Rough	Roughs
Harley Gum	Arlingham
Hartpury Green	
Hastings	
Hatherley Squash	
Hellens Early	Sweet Huffcap
Hellens Green	
Hendre Huffcap	Yellow Huffcap
Heydon	
High Pear	
Hillend Green	Ford's Green Huffcap
Holmer	Cluster Top, Startle Cock
Honey Knob	
Iron Sides	
Jenkins' Red	
Judge Amphlett	
Knapper	Napper
Late Hay Pear	Hay Pear
Late Treacle	
Lullam	
Lumber	Lumber Reds, Steelyard Balls, Steelyer Balls, Swaycots, Cumber
Margaret	
Merrylegs	
Moorcroft	Malvern Hills, Stinking Bishop, Choke Pear, Chokers
Murrell	
Nailer	Billy Williams
Newbridge	White Moorcroft
New Meadow	Lintot, Yokehouse
Oldfield	Ollville, Oleville, Offield, Awrel, Hawfield
Painted Lady	
Parsonage	
Pig Pear	
Pine	
Pint	Pine
Potato Pear	
Red Huffcap	Huffcap, Uffcap, Uffcup
Red Longdon	Red Longley, Red Longney, Brockle, Brockhill, Cide Pear, Aylton Red, Blunt Red, Red Horse

The following varieties of pears are perry pears

Variety	Synonym(s)
Rock	Mad Pear, Mad Cap, Black Huffcap, Brown Huffcap, Red Huffcap, Huffcap, Uffcap, Uffcap
Rumblers	Jug Rumbles, Rumble Jumble
Sack	
Sickle Pear	American Sickle
Silver Pear	Summer Pear
Snake Pole	
Sow Pear	
Speart Pear	
Staunton Squash	Squash Pear, White Squash
Stinking Bishop	
Swan Egg	Swan
Taynton Squash	
Teddington Green	Teddingtons
Thorn	
Thurston's Red	Dymock Red, Billy Thurston
Tumper	Tum, Tom, Tump
Turner's Barn	Longstalk
White Bache	Bache'sWhite, Beech White, White Beech
White Longdon	Longdon, Longland(s), Bastard Barland, Dandoe, Garradine, Port
Winnal's Longdon	Longdon, Longland(s)
Yellow Huffcap	Huffcap, Uffcap Uffcup, Brown Huffcap, Black Huffcap, Green Huffcap, Kings Arms, Yellow Longdon, Yellow Longland(s), Chandos Huffcap
Young Heydon	

APPENDIX II

Pear Collection at Brogdale Horticultural Trust 1997

Pear Cultivar	Season	Pear Cultivar	Season
Abas Beki	Early	Beth	Early
Abbé Fétel	Mid	Beurré Alexandre Lucas (3x)	
Admiral Gervais	Late	(mutation Lucas Bronzee)	Late
Alexandre Delfosse	Mid	Beurré Lucas Bronzee	Late
Alexandre Lambre	Mid	Beurré Baget	Mid
Alexandrina Bivort	Early	Beurré Baltet Pere	Mid
Alexandrine Douillard	Mid	Beurré Bedford	Mid
Alliance Franco-Russe	Mid	Beurré Bosc	
Alphonse Huttin	Late	(syn of Calebasse Bosc)	Mid
Ananas de Courtrai	Early	Beurré Brown	Mid
André Desportes	Early	Beurré Capiaumont	Mid
Antoine Bouvant	Late	Beurré Clairgeau (LA)	Mid
Arabitka	Early	Beurré d'Amanlis (3x)	Early
Arnold (Bartlett) (4x)(mutation of		Beurré d'Amanlis Panache	Early
Williams' Bon-Chrétien)	Early	Beurré d'Anjou (LA)	Late
Arpaval Ero	Early	Beurré d'Arenberg	Late
Aspasie Aucourt	Early	Beurré d'Avalon	Mid
Augusztusi Nagy	Early	Beurré d'Avril	Late
Autumn Bergamot	Mid	Beurré Davy	Mid
Autumn Nelis	Mid	Beurré de Beugny	Mid
Avocat Allard	Mid	Beurré Beurré de Conitz	Early
Ayrshire Lass	Early	Beurré de Jonghe	Late
		Beurré de L'Assomption	Early
Bambinella	Early	Beurré de Naghin	Late
Barney		Beurré Diel (3x)	Mid
Baronne de Mello	Mid	Beurré Dilly	Mid
Bartlett (syn of Williams'		Beurré Dubuisson	Late
Bon-Chrétien)	Early	Beurré Dumont	Mid
Beacon	Early	Beurré Duval	Mid
Belle de Bruxelles (Angers)	Late	Beurré Fouqueray	Mid
Belle de Jumet	Early	Beurré Francois	Mid
Bell des Abres	Late	Beurré Giffard (LA)	Early
Belle de Soignies	Late	Beurré Gris d'Hiver Nouveau	Late
Belle Guerandaise	Mid	Beurré Hardy (LA)	Mid
Belle Julie	Mid	Beurré Hardy	
Bellissime d'Hiver	Late	(mutation Red Beurré Hardy)	Mid
Bergamotte de Strycker	Late	Beurré Henri Courcelle	Late
Bergamotte Esperen	Late	Beurré Jean Van Geert	Mid
Bergamotte Fondant d'Été	Mid	Beurré Luizet	Mid
Bergamotte Heimbourg	Mid	Beurré Mortillet	Early
Bergamotte Philippot	Late	Beurré Papa la Fosse	Mid
Bergamotte Sannier	Late	Beurré Précoce Morettini (LA)	Early

Pear Collection at Brogdale Horticultural Trust 1997

Pear Cultivar	Season	Pear Cultivar	Season
Beurré Rance	Late	Clapp's Favourite (mutation Large Clapp's) (4x?)	Early
Beurré Six	Late		
Beurré Sterckmans	Late	Clapp's Favourite (mutation Starkrimson)	Early
Beurré Superfin	Mid		
Beurré Vauban	Late	Clara Frijs	Mid
Bianchettone	Early	Claude Blanchet	Early
Biggar Russet Bartlett (Mutation of Williams' Bon-Chrétien)	Early	Colette	Mid
		Colmar d'Été	Early
Bishop's Thumb	Late	Colonel Marchand	Late
Black Worcester (syn Warden Pear)	Late	Coloree de Juillett	Early
Blickling	Late	Comic Bodson	
Bon-Chrétien d'Hiver	Late	Comte de Lambertye	Early
Bon-Chrétien Frederic Baudry	Late	Comte de Lamy	Mid
Bon-Chrétien Walraevens	Early	Comte de Paris	Mid
Bonne d'Ezee (syn Brockworth Park)	Early	Concorde	Mid
Bonneserre de Saint-Denis	Late	Condo	Mid
Botzi Blanc	Early	Conference (EMLA)	Mid
Bristol Cross (LA)	Mid	Conference (Bronzee:B557)	Mid
Brockworth Park (syn of Bonne d'Ezee)	Early	Conference Primo	Mid
		Conference (Russet form:Wheldon)	Mid
Broompark	Late	Conference Van Wetten	Mid
Butirra	Late	Constant Lesueur	Mid
Butirra di Roma	Early	Coreless	Late
Butirra Rosata Morettini	Early	Coscia (France)	Early
Buzas	Early	Coscia di Donna	Early
		Coscia Précoce	Early
Calcina dal Corbel	Early	Coscia Tadiva	Mid
Calebasse Bosc (LA) (syn of Beurré Bosc)	Mid	Craig's Favourite	Early
		Crassane	Late
Canal Red	Mid	Crassane Panachee	Mid
Carrick	Mid	Crawford	Early
Cascade	Late	Csatar (syn of Soldat Laboureur)	Mid
Catillac (3x)(LA)	Late	Cserlevelo Csaszar	Late
Catillac (3x)(LA)	Late		
Cayuga	Mid	Dana's Hovey	Mid
Cedrata Romana	Mid	Dawn	Early
Certeau d'Automne	Mid	de Duvergnies	Mid
Chapin	Mid	Delbais (syn Super Comic Delbard)	Mid
Charles Ernest	Mid	Delices Cuvelier	Mid
Chaumontel	Late	de Sirole	Mid
Cheltenham Cross	Early	Directeur Hardy	Mid
Chojuro (Asian)	Early	Doctor Desportes	Mid
Cinq Crappes	Mid	Doctor Jules Guyot (LA)	Early
Citron des Carmes	Early	Doctor Lentier	Mid
Citron des Carmes Panache	Early	Doctor Lucius	Mid
Clapp's Favourite	Early	Doctor Stark	Early

Pear Collection at Brogdale Horticultural Trust 1997

Pear Cultivar	Season	Pear Cultivar	Season
Dorsel	Late	Figue d'Alencon	Late
Double de Guerre	Late	Fin de Siecle	Mid
Double Williams (4x) (mutation of		Fin Juillet	Early
Wiliams' Bon-Chrétien)	Early	Fiorenza	Mid
Doyenné Blanc (False)	Mid	Jargonelle (3x)	Early
Doyenné Boussoch (3x)	Mid	Jazzolo	Early
Doyenné d'Alencon	Late	Jean Cottineau	Early
Doyenné de Montjean	Late	Jean De Witte	Late
Doyenné de Poitiers	Mid	Jean d'Arc (LA)	Late
Doyenné d'Été	Early	Johnny Mount	Late
Doyenné d'Hiver		Josephine de Malines (M211)	Late
(syn of Easter Beurré)	Late	Jules d'Airolles	Mid
Doyenné du Comice (ELMA)	Mid		
Doyenné du Comice		Kelway's King	Mid
(mutation Red Comice)	Mid	Kis Margit	Early
Doyenné du Comice (4x?)	Mid	Knock-out Russet Bartlet (mutation	
Doyenné Georges Boucher	Mid	of Willaims' Bon-Chrétien)	Early
Dubbele Kreeftpeer	Mid	Kokhmasy	Early
Duchesse Bererd	Mid	Koonce	Early
Duchesse d'Angouleme	Mid	Kruidenierspeer	Early
Duchesse de Bordeaux	Late	Krystali	
Durondeau (LA)	Mid		
Dutch Holland	Mid	Laird Lang	Mid
		Large Clapp's (mutation of	
Early Seckel	Early	Clapp's Favourite (4x?)	Early
Early Seckel (4x?)	Early	Lawson	Early
Easter Beurré		Laxton's Early Market	Early
(syn Doyenné d'Hiver)	Late	Laxton's Foremost	Early
Egri	Late	Laxton's Record	Mid
El Dorado	Mid	Laxton's Superb	Early
Eletta Morettini	Late	Laxton's Superb	
Émile d'Heyst (LA)	Mid	(mutation Mercer (4x)	Early
Enfant Natais	Mid	Laxton's Victor	Mid
English Bergamot	Mid	Le Brun	Mid
English Caillot Rosat	Early	Le Curé (3X)(LA)	
Epine du Mas	Late	(syn of Vicar of Winkfield)	Late
Espiki	Early	Lee	Late
Eva Baltet	Mid	Legipont	Mid
Ewart	Mid	Lehoux-Grignon	Late
Eyewood	Mid	Le Lectier	Late
		Lemon	Mid
Fair Maid	Early	Leonie Bouvier	Early
Farmingdale	Mid	Lepoardo	Mid
Fauvanelle	Late	Levard	Late
Ferdinand Gaillard	Mid	Lord Mountnorris	Early
Fertility	Mid	Lorinc Kovacs	Mid

Pear Cultivar	Season	Pear Cultivar	Season
Louise Bonne de Printemps	Late	Moonglow	Early
Louise Bonne of Jersey	Mid	Mora	Mid
Louise Bonne Sannier	Mid	Moyer Russet Bartlett (mutation of	
Lucas Bronzee (mutation of		Williams' Bon-Chrétien)	Early
Beurré Alexandre Lucas)	Late	Mrs Seden	Late
Mac	Early	Napoleon	Mid
Madam Ballett	Late	Nar Armud	Late
Madame Millet	Late	Nargilia	Mid
Madame Treyve	Mid	Nec Plus Meuris	Late
Mademoiselle Solange	Early	Nectarine	Mid
Madernassa	Late	Niitaka (Asian)	Mid
Maggie	Early	Nijisseiki (syn Twentieth Century)	
Magnate	Mid	(Asian)	Mid
Magness	Early	Nimrod	
Magness (4x:2-4)	Early	Nobel	Late
Magyar Kobak	Mid	No Blight	Early
Maltese	Early	Nouveau Poiteau (LA)	Mid
Manning Miller	Mid	Nouvelle Fulvie	Late
Marechal de Cour (3x)	Mid	Nurun Burun	Mid
Marguerite Marillat	Early	Nyari Kalman	Early
Marie Benoist	Late	Nye Russet Bartlett (Mutation of	
Marie-Louise	Mid	Williams' Bon-Chrétien)	Early
Marie-Louise d'Uccle	Mid	Oktyabrzskaya	Mid
Marlioz	Late	Oldfield	Mid
Marquise	Mid	Old Home (4x?)	Mid
Martin Sec	Late	Olivier de Serres	Late
Maxine	Early	Onward (EMLA)	Mid
Max Red Bartlett (mutation of		Orel (15)	
Williams' Bon-Chrétien)	Early	Ovid (LA)	Late
Mellina	Late		
Mercedes	Late	Packham's Triumph (LA)	Mid
Mercer (mutation of Laxton's		Palkonyai Cukor	Mid
Superb) (4x)	Early	Parburton (Bartlett:4x) mutation	
Mere Perrier	Late	of Williams' Bon-Chrétien)	Early
Mericourt	Mid	Parrot Pear	Mid
Merton Pride (3x)(LA)	Early	Passe Colmar	Mid
Merton Star (N6802/3B)	Mid	Passe Crassane (LA)	Late
Messire Jean	Mid	Patten	Mid
Mezes	Early	Pero Nobile	Mid
Michaelmas Nelis	Mid	Peter	Mid
Mirandino Rosso	Early	Petite Marquerite	Early
Miskolci	Mid	Petrovka	Early
Molinaccio	Early	Phelps	Mid
Monarch	Late	Philippe Courvreur	Mid
Monsallard	Early	Philippe Chauveau	Early

Pear Cultivar	Season	Pear Cultivar	Season
Pierre Corneille (Angers)	Mid	San Lazzaro Selvatico	Mid
Pitmaston Duchess (3X)	Mid	Santa Claus	Late
Poirier Fleurissant Tard	Mid	Sant Maria (Bakker)	Early
Porporata	Early	Satisfaction	Early
Précoce de Trévoux	Early	Scipiona	Late
Précoce de Trévoux (Knuth)(4X)	Early	Seckel (Robarts)	Mid
President Barabe	Late	Seigneur Esperen	Mid
President d'Osmonville (SidneyB.C.)	Mid	Sheldon	Mid
President Drouard	Late	Shinsui (Asian)	Mid
President Heron	Late	Sierra	Late
President Mas	Mid	Sini Armud	Late
Princess (Sidney B.C.)	Mid	Sir Harry Veitch	Early
Princeipessa Yolanda Margharita	Late	Sirrine	Early
Provisie	Early	Solaner	Early
Pultency	Mid	Soldat Laboureur (syn of Csatar)	Mid
Pushkiniskaya	Early	Sos	Late
		Southworth	Mid
Redbald (mutation of		Souvenir de Jules Guindon	Late
Williams' Bon-Chrétien)	Early	Souvenir du Congrès	Early
Red Beurré Hardy (mutation of		Spadona d'Estate	Early
Beurré Hardy)	Mid	Spartlet	Mid
Red Comice (LA)(mutation of		Spinacarpi	Late
Doyenné du Comice)	Mid	Star	Early
Reimer Red	Mid	Starking Delicious	Early
Reine des Poires	Early	Starkrimson (mutation of	
Reliance	Early	Clapp's Favourite)	Early
Remy Chatenay	Late	Striped William (mutation of	
Revesz Balint dr	Early	Williams' Bon-Chrétien)	Early
Richard Peters	Early	Sucree de Montlucon	Late
Ritson	Mid	Suffolk Thorn	Late
Robin	Early	Summer Bergamot	Early
Roem van Wijngarden	Mid	Summer Beurré d'Arenberg	Early
Rogue Red	Late	Super Comice Delbard	
Roosevelt	Mid	(syn of Delbais)	Mid
Rosired	Early	Surprise	Mid
Royale d'Hiver	Late	Swan's Egg	Late
Rubiette d'Angers	Late	Szegenyek	Mid
Russet Bartlett (mutation of			
Williams' Bon-Chrétien)	Early	Tany Kisil	Early
		Tettenhall Dick	
Sainte-Anne	Early	Theodore van Mons	Mid
Saint-Jean Panachee	Early	Thompson's	Mid
Saint Luke	Early	Thornley	Mid
Saint-Remy	Late	Triomphe de Jodoigne	Mid
Sandar (Wm. Creuse)	Early	Triomphe de Vienne	Early
San Giovanni	Early		

Pear Collection at Brogdale Horticultural Trust 1997

Pear Cultivar	Season
Twentieth Century (syn of Nijisseiki) (Asian)	
Tyson	Early
Uvedale's St Germain (3x)	Late
Van Mons Leon Leclerc	Mid
Varginella	Late
Verbelu	Early
Vermont Beauty	Mid
Vicar of Winkfield (3x) (LA) (syn of Le Curé)	Late
Virgoloso	Late
Virgouleuse	Late
Volpina	Late
Voros Buza	Early
Warden Pear (syn of Black Worcester)	Late
White Doyenné	Mid
William Précoce Morettini	Early
Williams' Bon-Chrétien (EMLA) (syn Bartlett)	Early
Williams' Bon-Chrétien (EMLA) (Compatible)	Early Early
Williams' Bon-Chrétien (mutation Arnold) (Bartlett:4X)	Early
Williams' Bon-Chrétien (mutation Biggar Russet Bartlett)	Early
Williams' Bon-Chrétien (mutation Double Williams) (4x)	Early
Williams' Bon-Chrétien (mutation Knock-out Russet Bartlett)	Early
Williams' Bon-Chrétien (mutation Max Red Bartlett)	Early
Williams' Bon-Chrétien (mutation Moyer Russet Bartlett)	Early
Williams' Bon-Chrétien (mutation Nye Russet Bartlett)	Early
Williams' Bon-Chrétien (mutation Parburton)(Bartlett)(4x)	Early
Williams' Bon-Chrétien (mutation Redbald)	Early
Williams' Bon-Chrétien (mutation Russet Bartlet)	Early
Williams' Bon-Chrétien (mutation Striped Williams)	Early

Pear Cultivar	Season
Williams d'Hiver	Late
Williams d'Hiver	Late
Willie Peddie	Mid
Windsor	Early
Winter Nelis (LA)	Late
Winter Orange	Late
Worden Seckel	Mid
Zephirin Gregoire	Late
Zoe	Late

Seedlings, Species and Unknown Cultivars

	Season
Barnham 1	Mid
Carrier 1	Mid
Crichton-Maitland 1	Mid
EM 19 (Louise Bonne of Jersey x Conference)	Early
Fagg 1	Mid
Hermansverk 1/1	Late
Hermansverk 2/11	Mid
Hill 1	Late
Howlett	Early
Illinois 3-142 (4x)	Mid
Illinois 38	
Instone 1	
Italy 154 (Beurré Hardy x Roosevelt)	Mid
Italy 1437 (Sidney B.C.) (Doyenné d'Hiver x Passe Crassane)	Late
JI 552 (Doyenné du Comice x Williams' Bon-Chrétien)	Late
JI 3807 (Glou Morceau x Improved Fertility)	Early
JI 3884 (Doyenné du Comice x Double Williams)	Mid
JI 3897 (Doyenné du Comice x Double Williams)	Mid

Seedlings, Species and Unknown Cultivars

JI 4244 (Doyenné du Comice x Beurré Bedford)	Mid
Kieffer 1 (LA)	Late
Kieffer 4 (LA)	Late
NFT 102 (Laxton's Superb x Glou Morceau)	Mid
NFT 105 (Laxton's Superb x Doyenné du Comice)	Mid
NFT 106 (Laxton's Superb x Doyenné du Comice)	Late
NFT 107 (Laxton's Superb x Glou Morceau)	Late
NFT 108 (Laxton's Superb x Glou Morceau)	Late
Norman 1	Mid
Plymouth pear (Pyrus cordata)	
Pritchard 1	Early
Purdue 41	
Pyrus betulaefolia	
Pyrus cordata (Plymouth Pear)	
Smith 1	Late
Stanford	Late
Turner 1	Late
Unknown: S R Peart	Mid

Perry Pears

Barland
Barnet
Blakeney Red
Brandy
Butt
Gelbmostter
Gin
Green Horse
Hellen's Early
Hendre Huffcap
Judgee Amphlett
Moorcroft
Oldfield
Parsonage
Sweet Huffcap
Taynton Squash
Thorn
Wassenbirne
Winnal's Longdon
Yellow Huffcap

APPENDIX III

Pear Collection at R.H.S. Garden Wisley 1997

Pear Cultivar	Season
André Desportes	Sept
Baronne de Mello	Oct
Belle de Soignies	Dec
Belle Guerandaise	Oct-Nov
Belle Julie	Oct-Nov
Bellisime d'Hiver	Dec-Mar
Bergamotte d'Automne	Oct-Dec
Bergamotte Esperen	Jan-Mar
Beth	Sept
Beurré Alexandre Lucas	Nov-Jan
Beurré d'Amanlis	Sept
Beurré d'Anjou	Nov-Jan
Beurré d'Arenburg	Nov-Jan
Beurré Bachelier	Nov-Dec
Beurré Bedford	Oct-Nov
Beurré Bosc	
Beurré Capiaumont	Sept-Oct
Beurré Clairgeau	Nov-Dec
Beurré de Jonghe	Dec-Jan
Beurré Diel	Oct -Dec
Beurré Dumont	Nov-Dec
Beurré Dumortier	Oct-Nov
Beurré Fouqueray	Oct-Nov
Beurré Giffard	Aug
Beurré Hardy	Oct
Beurré Henri Courcelle	Nov-Dec
Beurré Jean van Geert	Oct-Nov
Beurré Précoce	
Beurré Rance	Dec-mar
Beurré Six	Nov-Dec
Beurré Sterckmans	Nov-Jan
Beurré Superfin	Oct
Bishops Thumb	Oct-Nov
Black Worcester	Dec-Apr
Bonne de Beugny	Oct
Bristol Cross	Sept-Oct
Brockworth Park	Sept
Butirra Précoce Morettini	
Callebasse Bosc	Sept-Oct
Canal Red	
Cascade	
Catillac	Dec-Apr

Pear Collection at R.H.S. Garden Wisley 1997

Pear Cultivar	Season
Charles Ernest	Oct-Nov
Clapps Favourite	Sept
Colette	
Colmar d'Été	Sept
Comte de Lamy	Oct-Nov
Comte de Paris	
Conference	Oct-Nov
Crawford	Aug
Dr Jules Guyot	Sept
Double de Guerre	Dec-Feb
Doyenné d'Alencon	Dec-Feb
Doyenné Blanc	Sept-Oct
Doyenné Bussoch	Sept-Oct
Doyenné d'Été	July-Aug
Doyenné Georges Boucher	Dec-Mar
Duchesse d'Angouleme	Oct-Dec
Durondeau	Oct-Nov
Émile d'Heyst	Oct-Nov
Eva Baltet	Oct
Fertility	Oct
Flemish Beauty	Sept
Fondante d'Automne	Sept-Oct
Fondante Thirriot	Sept-Oct
Forelle	Nov-Jan
Dieser Wilderman	Oct-Nov
Gorham	Sept
Green Pear of Yair	Sept-Oct
Hacon's Incomparable	Sept-Nov
Hessle	Oct
Huyshe's Prince of Wales	
Huyshe's Victoria	Dec-Jan
Improved Fertility	Sept-Oct
Jargonelle	Aug
Jules d'Airolles	Oct-Nov
Laxtons Progress	Sept
Le Brun	Oct
Legipont	Oct-Nov
Le Lectier	Dec-Jan
Louise Bonne of Jersey	Oct
Madernassa	
Madame Treyve	July-Sept
Magnate	Oct-Nov
Magness	
Marguerite Marillat	Sept
Marie Louise	Oct-Nov

Pear Collection at R.H.S. Garden Wisley 1997

Pear Cultivar	Season
Marie Louise d'Uccle	Oct
Merton Pride	Sept
Michaelmas Nelis	Sept
Nouveau Poiteau	Nov
Onward	Sept
Orcas	
Packham's Triumph	Nov-Dec
Passe Colmar	Nov-Dec
Pierre Corneille	Oct
Pitmaston Duchess	Oct-Nov
Roosevelt	Oct-Nov
Rosemarie	
St. Germain	Dec-Jan
Seckle	Oct-Nov
Souvenir du Congrès	Sept
Sucree de Montlucon	Oct
Swan's Egg	Oct
Thompson's	Oct-Nov
Triomphe de Vienne	Sept
Verdi	
Williams Bon Chrétien	Sept
Winter Nelis	Nov-Jan

INDEX

INDEX

INDEX

INDEX

INDEX